HIGHWAYS OF THE HEART

A brief alphabetical tour
of the physical and spiritual heart

JIM PARRATT

*God be in my heart
and in my thinking*

British Library Cataloguing in Publication Data:

a catalogue record for this publication

is available from the British Library

ISBN   978-1-912052-48-6

Typeset in 11.5pt Minion Pro at Haddington, Scotland

Printed by West Port Print & Design, St Andrews

CONTENTS

Dedication iv

Acknowledgements v

Foreword vi

The Heart (Da Vinci) viii

Introduction – the AMAZING HEART 1

A is for the ANXIOUS HEART 10

B is for the BROKEN HEART 15

C is for the CONSISTENT HEART 19

D is for the DISEASED, DAMAGED HEART 23

E is for the EXERCISED HEART 29

F is for the FAILING HEART 35

G is for the GENEROUS HEART 41

H is for HOT AND COLD HEARTS 46

I is for INSIDE THE HEART 50

J is for the JOYFUL, HAPPY HEART 55

K is for the KEPT, GUARDED HEART 62

L is for the LISTENING HEART 73

M is for the MUSICAL HEART 78

N is for the NOURISHED HEART 89

O is for the OPEN HEART 94

P is for PROTECTION (SALVAGE, SALVATION) 100

Q is for the QUIET, PEACEFUL HEART 109

R is for the RESISTANT, HARDENED HEART 117

S is for HEART STOP 121

T is for the TRANSPLANTED HEART 127

U is for the UPSET, FEARFUL, TROUBLED HEART 134

V is for VULNERABLE – AGEING AND THE HEART 142

W is for the WORRIED, STRESSED HEART 148

X is for the UNKNOWN, the CROSS and LOVE 156

Y is for YOUR EXAMINED HEART 165

Z is for A to Z – the LOVING, COMPASSIONATE HEART 169
OF GOD

'The Eyes of the Heart' by Daniel Hough 175

The book title 'Highways of the heart' comes from Psalm 84:5 which, in the English Standard Version (ESV) reads, 'Blessed are those whose strength is in you, in whose heart are the highways'.

DEDICATION

This book is for Pamela Joan Lyndon Parratt nee Marels of the clan Cuming, my wife of over sixty years, and from whom I have learnt so much about faith and of the 'heart of love'. In Pascal's words, 'there you have what faith is: God sensed by the heart'.

ACKNOWLEDGEMENTS

I am grateful to the many people who helped in the writing of this book. To readers of my first book (*Marvellously Made*) who encouraged me in this attempt to write another, to the Revd Norman Cruickshank and Dr John McArthur who read some of the initial and very early draft chapters, to my eldest son Stephen Parratt for his help with the topic of spiritual exercise, to my grandson Daniel Hough (@h_o_u_g_h) for the design of the book cover, to Bishop Timothy Dudley-Smith for much delightful correspondence and for his ready permission, and that of the Oxford University Press, to reproduce three of his insightful hymns. Also to András Simon of the Simon Galeria in Budapest for the line drawings. Then to my poetic and patient publisher Jock Stein of the Handsel Press for taking the risk of producing this small volume with the reminder that, as Dr Paul Brand once wrote, 'old age is the time to take risks'!

Very special thanks go to Susan Campbell (Scribblers . . . of Bearsden) for her omnicompetent help in the organisation of the manuscript and without whom it could never have reached a stage suitable for publication. Last, but certainly not least, to my friends and colleagues in heart research with whom I have collaborated in different ways over very many years, including (through the EU Scientific Network on Cardioprotection): Jutta and Wolfgang Schaper (Bad Nauheim), Jean-Claude Stoclet (Strasburg and Paris), Boja Ostadal and Frank Kolar (Prague). Also, to former colleagues Richard (Dick) Marshall and Brian Furman (Glasgow) and especially to Agnes Vegh for those delightful and somewhat productive laboratory days spent in our favourite Hungarian city, Szeged. To all heartfelt thanks!

FOREWORD

Historians have pointedly remarked that the three greatest books in the English language were all written within a short time span in the 17th century. The King James authorised version (AV) of the Bible (1611), the folio edition of Shakespeare's plays (1623) and William Harvey's volume on the human circulation of the blood, *De Motu Cordis* (1628). It has also been said that what the King James Bible is to the Christian church, and the Shakespeare folio is to English letters, so *De Motu Cordis* is to medicine worldwide. High praise indeed and surely no exaggeration!

All three have played a major role in my own life but what is of especial interest to me is the close association, at least in historical time, between the Bible and Harvey's book on the heart and circulation. This is because a good proportion of my life, indeed over forty years, has been spent thinking and working on various aspects of heart function (regulation of coronary blood flow, protection of the heart against damage and acute disorders of cardiac rhythm) and because, since my student days, my life has been coloured (usually brightly!) by my Christian faith and daily study of Scripture.

It has intrigued me that the bible has much to say about the 'heart'. Indeed, in Young's Bible Concordance there are nearly a thousand references to some aspect of that word. Can these two, I wondered, the scientific and the theological, be 'married' together? Does thinking about the physical heart, and the problems associated with damage to it, 'trigger' reflections (I would not dare to call them 'insights') on the heart as recorded in Scripture?

One way of attempting this that came to mind was to use a kind of heart A to Z. There are problems with this approach; for example, there are not many words in the English language, including in the Bible, beginning with the letters X and Z. There is however a scriptural warrant for this approach; Psalm 119 is the greatest of the alphabetic acrostic psalms. I did toy with the idea of setting aside difficult letters, following the example of the psalmist in omitting certain letters of the alphabet, along the lines of the 'broken' alphabetic acrostic in, for example, Psalms 9 and 10. Here the author not only missed some letters out but rearranged those that remained! In the end I decided to attempt to include all the letters from A to Z; whether successful or not I leave the reader to judge. And, there are other, more personal reasons! In a sense it was the alphabet that brought me to consider, and then accept, the Christian gospel and it was also through the alphabet that I discovered my wife. But that is another story!

This small book is not written with scientists in mind, medical or otherwise but with the euphemistically called, and rapidly diminishing, 'person in the pew'. Such may be tempted to skip over the initial 'scientific' section associated with each letter. However, I hope not. It would be good, I think, for those without a scientific background to attempt to learn just a little about the wonderful organ that sits comfortably inside our chest cavity. It is a thing of wonder! My hope is that we may delight in this mechanical pump that drives life-giving blood around our bodies and, as a result, grow closer to the heart of the One to whom we owe this 'little old heart within'.

Two other things. First, this is not a book to read from beginning to end! Let me rephrase that! No need to start at A and work your way through to Z. Be selective. Start (and finish) where you like. Some, like me, like to begin at the end! Secondly, you will see there are many references to Scripture. I make no apology for that; these are far more important than the text itself. And, it is easy to read the text without referring to them. But please do – maybe at a second reading?

And, as to the author, 'a writer, as he grows old, develops new thoughts, enlarges his vocabulary, varies his style according to the occasion which leads him to write with the intensity of his own emotions'. That was certainly my hope!

Jim Parratt (Bearsden, July 2019)

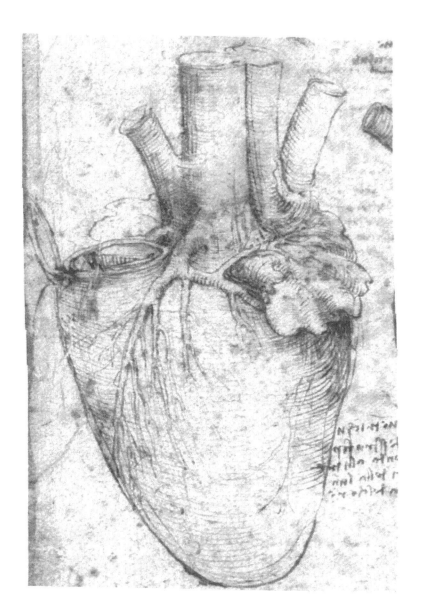

Your heart looks something like this, even though this wonderful pen and ink drawing was made on blue paper, by Leonardo da Vinci, over five hundred years ago. Two things to notice: first, the blood vessels (sectioned) that enter and leave the heart (at the top) and second, the (left) coronary artery which courses over the surface of the heart. Later, all will be revealed!

Introduction – the AMAZING HEART

To get us started on the direction of travel
– about pumps and tubes
'The heart of the matter and the matter of the heart'.

A little while ago I was asked by one of my younger relations what the heart looks like because 'I've never seen one'! Well, certainly it is quite unlike the bilobed, invariably red, inverted triangle found, for example on Valentine's Day cards. The best picture I could find of the human heart was by Leonardo da Vinci, found among his last anatomical drawings of 1513. I had wondered whether, as he drew those sectioned large blood vessels (the aorta and the vena cava) entering and leaving the heart, how near he was to formulating a theory of the circulation of the blood. I think probably quite close. However, it was to William Harvey, over a hundred years later, that due credit is given to the discovery of the circulation of the blood. And, today the heart still retains its place in our hearts.

The heart is a hollow muscular organ situated in the chest (thoracic) cavity settled comfortably between the lungs, somewhat off-centre and to the left. It is about the size of a clenched fist, shaped, as in the de Vinci drawing, rather 'like a pine cone kernel or an inverted triangle' and covered by a membranous sack (the pericardium). The hollow parts consist of four chambers, above are two rather thin walled collecting chambers called auricles or atria and, below them two very muscular ventricles responsible for pumping blood around the lungs (the right ventricle) and the rest of the body (the left ventricle).

The continuous contractions (beats) of the heart are clearly discernible and occur on average almost 100,000 times a day, each beat pushing, squeezing about 80 millilitres of blood into the circulation: about 5 litres each minute or over 7,000 litres each day. For those still working in pints and gallons that is around 2,000 gallons daily (remembering that each gallon is equal to eight pints). My own heart, up to now, has pumped the equivalent of well over 200 million litres around my now ageing body, enough to fill several super-tankers or the small loch I can see from our living room window. So, we could say that the heart is reliable and dependable; beat follows beat follows beat. It just keeps going on and on! Wonderfully consistent. An amazing pump!

The rate at which this amazing heart beats is dependent on external circumstances, faster when a person is excited, angry or undergoing exercise, (up to 100 – 200 beats per minute in severe exercise) and down to well below 50 beats per minute during sleep – and when approaching death. This beating commences before birth, at around 22 days of conception (the beat can be detected at around five to six weeks) and continues, if you are healthy, for 80 or 90 years without interruption, a succession of beat after beat. That is the really amazing thing about the heart; not so much the rate but the succession, the consistency – one beat, then another, then another. Whilst you are asleep for example, some twenty thousand beats at a fairly steady rhythm, beat after beat. And, if it should stop, then we do too and that so fragile earthly life would be over. 'If I should die before I wake, I pray the Lord my soul to take'.

In my favourite book on the heart[1] Dr Ted Bianco refers to the heart rate of hummingbirds, shrews, whales and clams. I do not have personal experience of any of these species but the facts he quotes are fascinating. For example, hummingbirds when feeding have a basic heart rate of about 1,000 a minute (falling to just about 50 when resting) whilst the rate of the Etruscan Shrew can reach a record breaking 1,511 beats a minute! One marvels at the way the moving parts can reach such a rate. At the other end of the scale the clam has the record for the slowest heart rate of all – 2 times a minute but increasing to 20 when excited! A blue whale (weighing around 100,000 kilograms) has a heart, about one metre in length, which chugs along at about 20 beats each minute – but it does live for something like 100 years compared to just one year for the shrew! Yet the hearts of both, the big and the small, during their lifetimes, pump about the same volume (millions of litres) of blood around their bodies. For all animals however the wonder is the succession rather than the rate.

This succession, beat after beat throughout life, is really astonishing! You can do the 'simple' rough calculation (perhaps in your head?) of how many times your heart has beat during your lifetime. At eighty years old for example perhaps well over two thousand million times; a figure that is about the same as the combined populations of France, Germany, Italy, Russia and the UK! And, all without stopping. And usually without any MOT. Impressive! And, if that heart stopped for just three to five minutes your life would be over.

---

1   James Peto (ed.), *The Heart*, Welcome Collection, London 2007.

2

Basically, your heart functions as a powerful pump pushing blood around the body in a ceaseless, circular flow, at considerable pressure and in a few seconds. If a major artery is accidentally severed (as the author knows to his cost) that blood jet could rise three or four feet in the air; stem that flow quickly! Everyone has a thumb! The heart is enabled to pump so effectively because its walls are made up of muscle; when excited the heart contracts, so the muscle shortens and thickens, thus squeezing on the hollow ventricles, the blood within being pushed forward into the major blood vessels (the aorta and the pulmonary artery). The valves at the entrance to these large vessels open to allow only forward flow, closing to prevent blood regurgitating back into the heart cavities.

This wonderful organ is actually two pumps working in parallel. The left ventricle pushes blood all the way around the body (all the way from top to toe) whilst the right ventricle is responsible for supplying blood to the lungs, where the blood gives up carbon dioxide in exchange for oxygen. This gas exchange can be seen in the colour difference between the blood entering the pulmonary arterial circulation, which is venous blood coming from the rest of the body where it has released oxygen, and that leaving the lungs. The former is dark blue (although it still contains significant amount of oxygen); the latter, returning blood from the lungs to the left side of the heart, is bright red. This marked colour difference was first shown as long ago as the end of the 17th century by the English physician Richard Lower. The difference can be seen too if a small artery is accidentally cut (as when occurs sometimes whilst shaving – bright red) compared to the dark blue venous blood arising from a severed vein.

There is also a marked difference in the pressures developed between the left ventricle (ejecting blood into the general circulation) and the right ventricle, which 'only' has to eject blood into the pulmonary (sometimes called the 'lesser') circulation, partly because the blood travels a shorter distance. This accounts for the difference in the pressures that need to be generated between the two ventricles; around 120 – 150 mmHg by the left ventricle compared to only about a third of this by the right ventricle. An everyday illustration. Inflating a bicycle tyre when completely flat does not require too much effort (pressure) to push air into the tyre (akin to the pressure in the pulmonary circulation); as the pressure within the tyre increases so is the effort required to 'pump up' to the required pressure is also much more; like the much higher pressure required to eject blood into the general (systemic) circulation. This difference in the pressures that need to be generated is reflected in the size: the amount of muscle in the respective ventricular walls is much thicker in the left than the right.

Cardiac muscle is specially adapted so that the electrical stimulus for contraction (called the cardiac action potential) is long, about a hundred times longer than that for skeletal muscle found, for example, in the limbs. This enables this wave to pass over the entire heart from one cell to the next (through so called 'gap junctions') in such a way that the heart contracts almost simultaneously, the rapidly contracting muscle cells transmitting their excitation rapidly to all the others. The electrical stimulus comes from a 'battery', called the sinus node situated in the wall of the right atrium; this leads first to atrial contraction and then, after a tiny fraction of a second delay (at the atrioventricular or AV node) the stimulus is forwarded to the ventricles. This electrical signal is projected to the body surface where it can be picked up by metal plates (leads) – the electrocardiogram (ECG).

The function of the 'pumping heart' is to supply blood to every living cell in the body. It does this through a system of vessels, the highly impressive circulation. This is a branching vascular tree with the blood first coursing through relatively large tubes (arteries) then through the smaller arterioles to terminate in a network of billions of microscopically tiny vessels, the capillaries. The blood contains everything each cell needs for functioning and for survival, it nourishes and cleanses. The blood is then returned back to the heart – all in a few seconds! The capillaries are in contact with the trillions of cells that make up our body. I well remember as a student watching, under a microscope, the capillary network in the web of the foot of an anaesthetised frog, observing the marvellous way the cells within the blood squeeze their way through such tiny vessels, giving up whatever the adjacent cells need, and then returning to the heart by way of small, and then ever larger veins. And so back to the heart to begin the journey all over again!

Incidentally, if it were possible to join all these various vessels end to end they would reach around 60,000 miles, almost two and a half times the distance around the equator. You might be wondering how much blood would be required to fill the body's whole circulatory system. Well, if all the vessels were to be open at the same time the heart would have to pump, not around five litres, but over forty litres per minute! For this to happen the heart would need to be considerably bigger. We would be all heart! One can imagine what such a body shape would look like! If all the vessels were dilated at the same time our hearts simply could not cope; the blood pressure would fall dramatically and the individual would bleed to death into his own blood vessels. Something akin to this actually happens in patients with sepsis and who then develop septic shock. The resultant fall in pressure, with the patient bleeding into their own veins, was at one time very difficult to counteract – until the cause was elucidated.

What is needed then is some means of regulation of the heart and blood vessels to enable it to adapt quickly to the varying needs of each individual part of the body. For instance, during exercise such as running or walking, the needs of the skeletal muscles of the lower limbs are most in need of blood, whilst at that time the requirements of the gut are not so important; what is needed then is more blood flow to the muscles of the legs, which is achieved by dilatation of the relevant vessels, and less blood flow to the gastrointestinal tract, which is achieved by narrowing (vasoconstriction) of the vessels to that organ. In the same way eating a meal puts more demand on the requirements of the gut thus requiring an increase in blood flow to this part of the body. This is achieved by dilatation of the supplying vessels whilst at the same time flow to other regions is reduced. As you read and think about these words then (hopefully!) there is an increase in brain (cerebral) blood flow to meet the substantial demands these words may impose on your 'thinking cells'. No need then for increases in gut or lower limb blood flow, unless you are eating, or running, at the same time as you are thinking! This remarkable ability to meet the varying needs of individual parts of the body by alterations in the diameter of the supplying vessels, so shifting blood around, is undertaken by nerves that are outwith the control of the will. These nerves are part of the 'autonomic' nervous system. Once again, all very remarkable! 'The wisdom of the body', to quote the American physiologist Walter Cannon.

So, in conclusion we can say that the heart is consistent, generous (all that blood pumped around the body, keeping back little for itself) and happy. Why happy? Simply because it is fulfilling the function for which it was created.

The Heart in Scripture

There are almost a thousand references to the heart in the Bible. We could attempt to break up this very large number into three main meanings of the word. Firstly, there are a few references to the beating heart situated within our chest cavity, the purely physical and wonderful pump concerned with the distribution of blood around the body, the heart described above.

Secondly, and this applies to the bulk of the references, the word is used as a kind of metaphor for the heart as the very essence of life, the 'inner man' since, by an easy transition, the word (*cardia* in Greek) came to stand for man's entire mental and moral activity, both the rational and emotional elements, the 'inner hidden springs of the personal life'. In other words, the heart is not just a lump of flesh responsible for one thing only, the pumping of blood around the body. The third use of the word 'heart' in Scripture refers to the heart of God, which we will think about at the end of the book.

1 The physical heart

First then, those biblical verses refer to the physical heart, although it is uncertain whether even these always mean the beating, pumping heart. The first of these comes in the story of Nabal which is recounted in 1 Samuel 25 and discussed more fully later in the chapters on the 'Resistant Heart' and 'Heart Stop'. In brief we are told that after a night of binge drinking, and some stern words from his wife, 'his heart died within him and became as stone'. But is it Nabal himself that turned to stone or his heart? Stroke or heart attack? Most probably death from a myocardial infarction in a heart damaged by alcohol abuse.

Rather similar accounts of 'sudden death' (cardiac?) come in the stories of Ananias and his wife Sapphira, 'who fell down and breathed their last'.[2] Perhaps also of Herod who, 'in the middle of an oration' was 'struck down by an angel of the Lord' and breathed his last.[3]

Other references are more specific. The first relates to the death of King David's elder son Absalom. The account is in 2 Samuel 18. Absalom rebelled against his father, wanting the kingdom for himself. After the battle that followed the crushed rebellion Absalom, in attempting to flee to safety, was caught up by his hair (his narcissistic glory) in the thick (central) branches of an oak (terebinth) tree. He was then ambushed and surrounded by 'ten men'. The leader of David's army, Joab ('I will not waste time') took three javelins (the word means sharp sticks) in his hand and thrust them into the heart of Absalom 'while he was still alive'.[4] There is a play on words here – the two hearts, one a vulnerable human organ, the other the dense 'centre' of

---

2   Acts 5:5, 10.

3   Acts 12:23.

4   2 Samuel 18:14.

the tangle of branches. Another example of the physical heart in Scripture is the account of the death of Jehoram, the son of King Ahab of Israel, by Jehu, commander of the army. At this treacherous meeting Jehu 'drew his bow at full strength and shot Jehoram between his shoulders such that the arrow pierced his heart and he sank in his chariot'.[5] No chivalry here; it seems he shot the fleeing Jehoram in the back.

However, another certain reference to the physical heart comes in the account of the death of Jesus on the Cross. After Jesus had died[6] one of the soldiers pierced his side with a spear, and 'at once there came out blood and water'. This was in fulfilment of the prophecy of Zechariah.[7] The American pathologist Dr William Edwards has pointed out that the word used for 'side' is *pleura*, suggesting that the sword thrust was into the chest cavity and thus directly into the heart. The 'water' could well have been pericardial fluid (the heart is enclosed in a sac that contains this fluid), the blood coming from the heart itself.

2 The spiritual heart, the centre of life

Of course, in common parlance there is another sense in which the word 'heart' is used. Not only that beating, pumping, muscular and 'deeply moving' organ inside our chest cavity but used figuratively of affection, love, feeling, courage as well as of the centre of things (a city, a lettuce!). We use words like hearty, heartache, heartfelt, heartless, heart-searching, 'with all one's heart'. We can be heartbroken but hopefully big-hearted. We 'learn by heart'. We might on occasions have heartburn, especially if we 'eat our heart out'.

In his book *Carrying the Heart*, the pathologist Professor Gonzalez-Crussi[8] raises the interesting question: 'Which comes first, the head or the heart'? How did the heart come to represent the seat of passions, of sensibility and emotion and in which reside charity, compassion, devotion and pity? This is true, in nearly all languages. There is also the idea that perception and understanding are part of the cognitive faculties of the heart and that this 'higher form of cognition' is a level of understanding superior to that purely

5 2 Kings 9:24.

6 John 19:33.

7 Zechariah 12:10.

8 Frank Gonzalez-Crussi, *Carrying the Heart: Exploring the Worlds Within Us*, Kaplan, New York 2009.

intellectual cognition acquired by the brain. The heart then has access to a form of awareness barred to the intellect. Cognition by the heart, knowledge impregnated with emotion. He quotes Pascal as saying 'the heart has reasons that reason does not know at all; we know this by a thousand ways'.

Two forms of 'knowing' then. Heart knowledge 'that feels God' and from the brain intellectual reason, a feeble, inferior form of knowledge, 'the cool light of a purely intellectual cognition' that keeps us at a distance. In contrast to the knowledge of the heart that engages us and draws us to the world; we receive 'with all our heart'. As the German philosopher Max Scheler wrote about the 'realm of the inner life', those who disregard this realm because it is independent of thought are 'like a man who has healthy eyes and closes them and wants to perceive colours with his ear or his nose'. Or as the great German conductor Wilhelm Furtwangler once said, 'you have to think with your heart and feel with your brain'.

Interesting too that one of the two Greek words associated with the physical heart (*cor*), hence coronary, the arteries that supply the heart muscle with blood, comes from the word (*cura*) for concern, for care, and that William Harvey, who discovered the circulation of the blood (see above) thought of the heart as 'the beginning and foundation of life', the 'author of all from which all vigour and strength flows, the ultimate symbol of human affection'.

The word translated 'heart' in both Hebrew and Greek then is a common metaphor for the 'inner man', the deep place where the real person dwells, the 'real you'. It is our identity, 'the man (person) himself'. It is the seat of knowledge, understanding and wisdom, a synonym for 'mind', the centre of consciousness and the will. It is the seat (the vital centre) the core, of human personality and character, of affections and desires, of thinking and intentions, the centre of our being where we are most ourselves, most real. It is the place where conscience dwells and where God's Spirit gains entrance or exclusion. For the Christian it is where Christ dwells, the heart centre of our spiritual lives. In Pascal's phrase 'it is the heart that feels God; there you have what faith is, God sensed by the heart'. It is thus the sphere of Divine influence, 'the hidden person of the heart'.

So, in anatomical terms the psychological focus in scripture is a step lower than in modern speech – which has mind for consciousness, thought and will and the heart for emotions. In the Bible, 'heart' is used more widely; the word does not distinguish between rational and mental processes. Or as Hamlet has it 'my heart's core, aye, in my heart within the heart'. Clearly then the word heart is a metaphor, a 'figure of speech' implying, but not explicitly stating, a comparison between two objects. Jesus was fond of these! He is shepherd, bread, light, a way, a vine. Christians are to be 'born again' and then to become 'the salt of the earth', although it is true that we are comprised partly of sodium chloride! But this is not plain language. A metaphor then is both what it says and what it does not say. It creates fresh meaning because it activates our imagination. In our God-directed imagination we can enter into the spiritual unseen that God's word opens to us. It is part of the delight we have in God's word, part of the 'chewing and masticating' to make it our own. There is something more, something beyond (ayont) to what can be seen, touched, heard or read.

Here are some examples from Scripture. Hearts can be soft or obstinate, stone hard, indeed diamond hard, they can be bitter or loving, closed or receptive, known or hidden (the 'hidden man of the heart'), evil or pure and cleansed. Hearts can sing, they can burn and melt, they can reason, they can be 'sprinkled' and made new, they are 'in the Lord's hands'. They can even be circumcised or uncircumcised! Imagine! The words of Jesus can 'live in our hearts'. Yet, other things can be hidden there too, that is in our hearts.

Clearly, none of the above is true of physical, beating hearts. They are metaphors, pictures, illustrations. The heart, in both these meanings, sustains life, the physical and the spiritual. Is it possible to tie these two meanings together, the cardiac pump and the 'hidden spring of the personal life'? How can a basic understanding of the hollow, muscular organ placed comfortably in the chest cavity between the lungs, shed any light on the meaning of the word in the Bible? This small book then is an attempt to link the two main meanings of this wonderful word; those things that can affect our physical hearts acting as a kind of 'trigger' for thinking about our spiritual hearts, our 'inner being'. Does an understanding of how this wonderful part of the human body functions shed light on its meaning in God's word? And, in this, we have the supreme example. We follow Jesus himself in the use of metaphor to explore spiritual truth; it becomes part of the language of people of faith. What we see in the world, accessible to our senses, by the use of metaphor, becomes an opening, a door to something invisible, inaudible, inaccessible to our senses.

Everything we do 'flows from the heart'.[9] So then, let us explore the heart!

---

9   Proverbs 4:23.

A is for the ANXIOUS HEART

'Anxiety weighs down the heart.'[1]
'Do not be anxious about anything but . . .'[2]

Not long ago I received an email from an elderly friend in Hungary, anxious about her heart. 'It feels as though my heart is trying to jump out of my chest! My heart is beating very fast; it is racing. It is a horrid feeling! It is unpleasant, disconcerting'. There was the feeling that 'something was not quite right' (as the ScotRail announcement has it about unattended packages left at stations or on trains). She was very much aware that her heart was doing 'something not quite right'. 'What is happening to my heart? Is it suddenly going to stop?' Apart from a high degree of anxiety, there were other symptoms as well. She was often breathless, she had difficulty in sleeping and was concerned about her health. Naturally, in turn her loved ones were anxious about her. Not surprising. After all the heart is an essential organ! By the way it should be pointed out that this is quite a different sensation to the increase in heart rate (the heart 'throb') that results from falling in love!

The clinical diagnosis for my friend's condition was atrial fibrillation (AF) or flutter, a fairly common abnormal heart rhythm especially in the elderly. It is where the heart beats at a very rapid, irregular and unpredictable rate, perhaps up to 100 beats/minute, detectable by checking your pulse. It is as though you are performing exercise – but you are not. You may struggle for breath, you begin to feel anxious and you sweat. Then, the next minute the rate is normal again. Atrial fibrillation then can sometimes be difficult to diagnose because it is often episodic, it can 'come and go'. This means it may require continuous assessment of cardiac electrical activity (the electrocardiogram) over a considerable time period, perhaps days. In such cases this technique (sometimes known as Holter monitoring) may pick up whether, and how often, disorganised atrial activity occurs. This can now also be monitored using a 'skin patch recorder'.

---

1   Proverbs 12:25.
2   Philippians 4:6.

Under normal resting conditions our heart beats at a fairly regular rate of 60 to 70 beats/minute. Of course, it can beat considerably faster when we are excited or performing some sort of exercise or in certain disease states, such as an overactive thyroid gland or following severe blood loss. The key difference is that with atrial fibrillation the rhythmical pattern and, in turn, normal cardiac contraction and relaxation, becomes uncoordinated. This is because the conduction of electrical impulses from the atria to the ventricles is no longer controlled: these impulses come not from the heart's 'control centre' (called the sinoatrial or SA node) but from another part of the atria. There is a new 'rogue' disorganised control centre sending impulses to the contracting ventricles.

There are consequences. First, the continuous swirling of the blood in the atria may create a blood clot (called a thrombus) which subsequently may then be swept into the general circulation. This thrombus may then obstruct a small vessel in the brain, resulting in a stroke, or in the coronary circulation where the result may be a myocardial infarction. In either case the result is cell death, in the brain or the heart, in those areas supplied by the now clot obstructed blood vessel. The other possible consequence is that the increase in heart rate, if it is persistent over a prolonged period, leads to the heart tiring, failing and, in the worst-case scenario, stopping altogether. No surprise then that people with AF often live with anxiety.

How can this condition be treated? Sadly, this type of rhythm disturbance is difficult to treat with drugs. Routine treatment consists of giving drugs to inhibit the possibility of clots forming in the atria including that old but truly amazing 'clot busting' drug aspirin. This is to inhibit intravascular coagulation within the fibrillating atria. In this condition aspirin is given in a much lower dose than that used to ease pain; less than half a normal 300mg tablet, which is more likely to be readily on hand, or a low dose tablet (75mg – although this dose too is unnecessarily high). Good idea to have one in your pocket. Other 'blood thinning' drugs such as warfarin are usually prescribed long term. The other treatment is to 'destroy' by 'burning' the local atrial focus of the arrhythmia using a technique called catheter ablation. Those patients with 'slow' AF will need a pacemaker fitted.

As far as I am aware there are no scriptural references to atrial fibrillation but there are many to anxiety. However, we should first define what we mean by this presently well used word. In the New Testament the word in Greek (*merimna*) basically means to be distracted; it refers to a mind pulled in different directions, to be full of 'care', insecure. It comes for example, when Jesus, explaining the meaning of the parable of the Sower[3] speaks of the 'cares of this world'. It comes again when Paul speaks of 'the daily pressure on me of my anxiety for all the churches'.[4] It is a distracting 'care' – 'do not be anxious about your life . . . your clothes'.[5] In this sense the word anxiety comes only a few times in Scripture. In the English language anxiety is akin to 'unease' or to fear especially about the future. We are unsettled. The unknowns and challenges leave us feeling anxious; a new job and colleagues, a new place to live and 'settle'. Some philosophers use the same word (or the Danish word 'angst') to refer to the frustration, indeed pessimism, about the whole human condition, the inexplicability of life. We live, as W.H. Auden wrote, in 'an age of anxiety'. When referred to the heart, to be anxious is usually to do with the sense that 'my heart is trying to jump out of my mouth' as in AF, or of sudden chest pain. In other words, the awareness of the possibility of an underlying cardiac problem. It seems that three out of four people with a heart condition are anxious about their health, about what might happen to them.

Scripture is quite clear about this condition of anxiety. We are not to be anxious. More easily said than done?

When the Old Testament speaks of anxiety in a man's heart it calls it a 'burden', a 'weight'.[6] It is detrimental to both our physical and spiritual lives. Spiritually this anxiety smothers, chokes God's word and prevents it finding a permanent dwelling place in our hearts.[7]

In the passage from Matthew referred to above[8] Jesus asks us to consider, to think about these anxieties in the light of what we know. We know that God cares, that God provides. We are asked to look around at the activities of God in nature (birds, flowers, grass), we are to 'notice carefully', to study closely, to seek first. When we do then we see that God cares and provides. There then follows the argument in the form of questions – 'are you not', 'which of you', 'why', 'will he not'. We are to take our knowledge of God's care and provision to heart. Think, he says, about how you have proved God's love in the past. We are to trust our heavenly Father in the knowledge that he

---

3   Matthew 13:22; Luke 8:14.
4   2 Corinthians 11:28.
5   Matthew 6:25, 28.
6   Proverbs 12:25.
7   Luke 8:14.
8   Matthew 6:25-34 .

knows about our needs. We are also to accept the things we cannot change, our height for example (a touch of the Lord's humour here) and trust God for the rest. If we can plan ahead then we are to do just that. But all the time trusting. The Scottish poet George MacDonald puts it this way – 'a man is perfect in faith when he can come to God with the weight of failures, neglects and wandering forgetfulness, and say to him you are my refuge'. 'Be still and know that I am God'. This is the essence of faith; to trust the God who knows what we need, who cares about us, who loves us and who provides for us because he is supremely able to do so. The essence of these passages in the gospels is 'first things first' – which is the kingdom of God – and then be sure of God's provision. This may not guarantee a life free from problems; but these need not be multiplied by being anxious about them, especially before they occur. It might never happen, but if it does God is still there, is still the same unchanging and loving heavenly Father.

We see this too in the well-known passage in Paul's letter to the Philippians chapter 4, where verse 6 is usually translated 'be anxious for nothing' (AV), 'about anything' (ESV), to be 'unduly concerned for'. Here the emphasis is on prayer; we are to 'tell God in every detail (everything, anything, all) our needs in earnest and thankful prayer' (v. 6, 7 Phillips), enumerating in his presence all the things that make us anxious. This involves careful planning and reflection leading to action (v. 8, 9). The answer to 'care' is then an outpouring of the heart to God, a positive entrusting of oneself and one's troubles to God. It is not inaction, not apathy. Positive action is required.

This too Peter, no stranger to anxiety, emphasises when he writes about 'casting' all our cares on God,[9] following the psalmist's example.[10] The word 'cast' is active, the same word as that used of the followers of Jesus 'casting' their cloaks on the colt as Jesus rode into Jerusalem. It is also used by the author of the letter to Hebrew Christians about not 'throwing away' your confidence.[11] So, there are things about anxiety we have to be and to do. We should humble ourselves under God's mighty hand, active yet submissive, aware of God's sovereignty and confident in his care, of his taking thought for us.[12] It means understanding and having faith in the God who is in control of all that happens to us, no matter what. Then we need to cast, to throw and to tell.

9 1 Peter 5:7.
10 Psalm 55:22.
11 Hebrews 10:35.
12 Psalm 40:17.

This 'telling' is important. We need to tell. It was a disaster when, at the wedding feast at Cana the wine ran short.[13] A serious matter indeed because, as the Jewish saying puts it 'without wine there is no joy'. A severe breach of hospitality was in the offing especially when we remember that Jewish weddings often lasted a week. Mary the mother of Jesus saw the problem: maybe this was a family wedding for which she had some responsibility. Was she somewhat anxious? Her response? She told Jesus. Very short, direct and to the point. 'They have no wine'. No advice given as to how to deal with the situation, just a simple statement of fact. Does this tell us anything about praying for others in times of anxiety? Sometimes, of course, we know quite a lot about the details of a particular situation from prayer letters or an immediate email; sometimes we know very little about the person or the circumstances. Is it required in intercessory prayer to tell our heavenly Father all those comprehensive details ('everything by prayer and supplication') which our Father knows only too well? Or should we simply bring that situation and person into the Lord's presence and simply tell – 'they have no . . .'. Often, we know rather little about the anxious situation in which those we have promised to pray for are in. We just know them, folk we love and are concerned for. I find helpful this prayer, the origin of which I am unsure. Here it is. 'Heavenly Father release into their (our) lives all that you see that they (we) need at this time'. And lift them into his presence. Tell and cast.

'Tell Jesus'. Tell your Heavenly Father about those troubles, those anxieties. Just tell.

---

13 John 2:1-11.

B is for the BROKEN HEART

'Our God . . . heals the broken-hearted
and binds up their wounds.'[1]

Is it really possible physically to suffer from a 'broken heart'? Lovesick, bereavement. Sadly, for some, just getting up in the morning is an effort of self-will, little appetite and almost falling apart. Emotionally then yes. But physically too? Yes, it is possible. Long-term feelings of grief, protracted sadness through the loss of a loved one can cause real injury to the heart. This is true for example especially of women of a certain age following exposure to sudden, unexpected emotional trauma. There are symptoms of chest pain, difficulties in breathing, irregular heartbeats, leading to deformation (ballooning) of the left ventricle and consequential difficulties in the heart functioning as a pump. In a very few cases the condition is fatal, through cardiac shock or 'sudden cardiac death' resulting from ventricular fibrillation.

This rare clinical condition, now known as takotsubo cardiomyopathy, was first described in Japan in 1991 and is a form of 'stress cardiomyopathy', reversible (usually) left ventricular dysfunction precipitated by any acute emotional trauma such as divorce or, especially, the loss of a loved one, a close family member. It is perhaps one reason why elderly couples can die within a short time of one another. Or, it could follow major surgery or national tragedies; the incidence was high following the major earthquake (6.8 on the Richter scale) that devastated Japan in 2004. Takotsubo is so named because the shape of the affected heart resembles a fishing pot or trap used for catching octopus (*takotsubo* in Japanese). It is now known to also occur in Western countries as a 'rare' (less than 3% incidence) condition presenting as a myocardial infarction but 'without evidence of coronary involvement'. However, not now as rare as was first thought; more than fifty cases were identified recently in Aberdeen resulting in permanent changes in the heart. A worldwide register of such patients

---

1   Psalm 147:3.

15

contains data on 1500 individuals. Ninety percent of these cases are in women.

The mechanisms are unknown but a sudden surge of the stress hormones called catecholamines (adrenaline, noradrenaline) seem the most likely explanation; similar changes in cardiac muscle have been observed experimentally following their prolonged administration. It is well known that catecholamine release is a consequence of emotional and physical stress – the 'flight and fight response'. Years ago, in the 1950's, working in the laboratory next to my own, two colleagues showed that patients with phaeochromocytoma (a tumour of the medulla of the adrenal gland, which is situated just above the kidney and in which catecholamines are produced) had very elevated blood levels of adrenaline and noradrenaline and that this leads to changes in the heart similar to those now found in takotsubo cardiomyopathy.

Many, most perhaps, have (or will have) experiences in life, situations that can only be described as devastating, shattering, heartbroken. The loss of a loved one, severe financial loss or the loss of a home or a job, news of a life-threatening illness, betrayal by someone close to us. We feel crushed by what is happening to us. A friend had suddenly to relocate from a missionary situation in which they had been involved for years. This led, on returning 'home' to unemployment. They felt like 'strangers in a strange land' – their own. There were consequences not only for them but for their children. Loss of friends, culture, language, income, years of spiritual investment. A crushing of their world. Broken. One of the illustrations of their condition, and the healing of it, was of a punctured and deflated bicycle inner tube; a suitable sealant can flow into that puncture and so avoid a sudden collapse. And what was that 'spiritual sealant'? As we will see it was, indeed is, God's word. Our hearts, like that punctured bicycle tyre are subject to being wounded, damaged, broken, punctured. Things happen that penetrate our defences, that deflate so that we are unable to move on. We grind to a halt. When our hearts break, God's word if we allow it, can fall into the cracks in our heart, helping to hold, bind together and heal.

Broken hearts are common in certain literature of a romantic kind and in popular lyrics, for example the Elvis Presley song 'Heartbreak Hotel', sadness and vulnerability packed into a couple of minutes. Or in George Bernard Shaw's play 'Heartbreak House'. In classical music there are numerous examples. I think of Schubert's song cycle 'Die schöne Müllerin' from 1823, twenty poems of moderate quality brilliantly set to music, which tell the simple story of a young man's love for 'the maid of the mill'. Each incident in the story is etched in songs which move from elation ('Dein ist mein Herz und soll es ewig ewig bleiben!' – My heart belongs to you and will remain so for ever) to the resentment of unrequited love (the girl, in the arms of another and lost forever) and then to a 'broken heart' ('Wo ein treues Herze in Liebe vergeht' – when a true heart perishes for love). Ending, the poetry is unclear, in death; 'Gute Ruh! Tu die Augen zu! Wandrer, die müder, du bist zu Haus' (rest well, close your eyes, tired wanderer, you are home). Lovesick, heart-broken, heart crushed, 'lost' (losing heart).

Scripture has many references to the 'broken hearted'. A right attitude to God begins with a broken and contrite heart, translated by Pamela Greenberg in her 'The book of prayer songs', as 'a crushed and shattered heart', words that could just as well describe the takotsubo physical heart. The 'broken heart' is the sacrifice God is looking for[2] and is symbolic of humility and penitence (a 'broken spirit'). Such brokenness is essential because it is the hard and stony heart (literally a heart 'covered with many stones') that does not submit to God's will.[3] The story of David, the author of Psalm 51 and recorded in 2 Samuel 11 and 12, is a good example. His life had always followed a trajectory of ups and downs and certainly, at this point in his life, the trajectory was downwards, descending into disaster, 'as thick as the arrows at Agincourt'. The sin of adultery with Bathsheba, the murder, planned by David, of her husband, now safely packed away in a body bag, then the death of his baby son, all led to genuine confession with no attempt to excuse his conduct. Broken-hearted. And, wonderfully, God's priceless forgiveness; the broken heart makes God's grace flow; the 'spiritual sealant'.

'The Lord is near to the broken-hearted, he saves the crushed in spirit.'[4] Here, when David was yet again in a life-threatening situation, fleeing from King Saul who was out to kill him, there was the assurance of the Lord's nearness. God is not distant. God is not only near to the broken-hearted, he 'heals' all such, he 'binds up' their wounds[5] because 'his understanding of us is beyond measure' (v. 5). And, healing means 'mending'. We are not like

---

2   Psalm 51:17.
3   Ezekiel 11:19.
4   Psalm 34:18.
5   Psalm 147:3.

Humpty Dumpty, who couldn't be put back together again, but 'you (God) are the one healing the shattered of heart, patiently binding their grief' (Greenberg). The OT word (*shabar*) usually means to smash, shatter, crush and is used of things; broken doors, vessels, swords, bones, yokes, idols and the tablets of the law,[6] but is also used figurately of a shattered heart..

In the NT a similar word is used of 'breaking bread' as in the Lord's Supper, of breaking the law, of a marriage bond or of a shipwreck. Of the twelve distinct Greek words so translated as broken or crushed (breaking in pieces by crushing) one is used metaphorically of a 'broken hearted person', crushed, as one would crush dried, dead leaves under foot in autumn. It is used of the agonies, ending in death, of the Lord Jesus 'bruised' (crushed) for our sins.[7] 'Now comes my hour of heart-break and what can I say? Father save me from this hour? Being in agony (broken) he prayed more earnestly'.[8] It is also the word used of the eventual crushing of Satan 'under foot'.[9]

Yet another Japanese word! There is an art form for mending broken pottery called 'kintsugi'. Gold dust mixed with resin is used to re-attach broken pieces and to fill in the remaining cracks. This makes the broken pot even more beautiful than the original! 'Beauty for brokenness' as the hymn puts it.

One reason for the coming of the Messiah is indeed to 'bind up' the broken-hearted, covering every kind of human breakdown. He still comes to the individual to do just that. Further, Jesus has 'broken down in his own flesh (the broken heart of Christ?) the dividing wall of hostility, creating a new man (with healed hearts), making peace, reconciling, giving us access to the Father, making us members of the household of God'.[10]

---

6 Exodus 32:19.

7 Isaiah 53:5,10.

8 Luke 22:42-44.

9 Romans 16:20.

10 Ephesians 2: 14-19.

C is for the CONSISTENT HEART

'A God of faithfulness.'[1]

I wonder how many of you have taken your own pulse – or that of somebody else? In all crime stories on television whenever there is a body, and in most TV crime stories there are many bodies even in the one episode, the first thing the detective or paramedic does is to 'check the pulse'. Can they find it? Is the person still alive? Yes, I can feel the pulse! Or, sadly not. That shake of the head. Now take your own pulse. Just to make sure you are still alive. With your right hand, curl your fingers around your left wrist; or over the major artery in your neck – although not too tight - and count, one, two, three, with your eye on the second hand of your watch. The rate is important, but even more important is the succession, how one beat is followed by another, then another. All the time. Throughout life. Consistently, constantly. The steady rhythm of your heart. Yet any one of those beats could be your last. When your heart stops you stop too. Life on earth will be over. We cannot 'will' our heart to continue to beat.

It is this consistency that is so remarkable. This constancy. Wonderful! Some simple maths! Have you ever done the calculation of how many times throughout life your heart has continued to beat? Of course, accuracy in this is impossible; you cannot keep your 'finger on the pulse' all the time! There are other things to do. But it is possible to best guess. Let us, for arguments sake, suppose you are thirty years of age, although there may be very few people of that age reading this book. How often in your life has your heart been beating? Simple mathematics! An average heart rate is 60 beats/minute so in one hour of your life it has beat 3600 times. In one day, 360 times 24 or 86,400 times. In one average month then about 2.6 million times; in one year about 36 million times, so in thirty years about 1000 million times! Check my sums! We say 'about' because your heart rate varies; slower in sleep for example, faster in emotional states

---

1   Deuteronomy 32:4.

and during exercise. Of course, if you are over eighty, like the author, then one would need to upgrade that figure significantly! More sums!

Our miraculous, life-giving hearts! Maintaining our blood circulation under all the diverse activities of daily life. And, all without stopping. No rest! Remarkable. Wonderful. Faithfully, dependably. Just beating. We have just a 'toehold on eternity'.

Now, what is even more remarkable is that with each beat your heart has pumped into the circulation about 70ml of blood; this is called the 'stroke volume'. So, in one minute the volume pumped is of the order of 5 to 6 litres; this is known as the 'cardiac output'. Incidentally, this figure is close to the total amount of blood in the body. So, in one hour your heart has pumped sixty times this, or about 3000 litres. Picture the litres of milk on the supermarket shelves. Probably nowhere near this figure. Now do some more simple (mental?) arithmetic. How much blood has your heart pumped in your lifetime? I'll leave that calculation to you! And, for most people without any kind of service. No MOT. What other kind of machine could do that? And then think about how far that pumped blood has travelled in your lifetime, remembering that there about 60,000 miles of blood vessels in your body, in some the blood travelling very fast (through the large vessels), sometimes much more slowly, as through the intricate minute capillary network. We are indeed, as the psalmist remarked, 'marvellously made'!

Our hearts then are, throughout life, consistent, persistent, regular, reliable, faithful even. And, in one sense, unchanging. The key word to describe the human heart within each one of us is consistent – beat after beat after beat. Dependable. Like the rest of nature. Day follows night, month follows month, summer follows spring which is, in turn, followed by autumn and winter. Year after year. The tides come in and go out, the steady succession of nap tides and spring tides is invariable. The leaves on the trees change colour and fall off. In winter the bulbs are asleep and, when the temperature increases, they come awake. The biological processes of life in nature, are constant, invariable, continual, habitual, at least in the sense that they remain essentially the same over a long time period. We ourselves are born, live and then die.

We can say that God can be described by all of these words; he too is consistent, true to who he is and to what he has said. He does not deviate. He is reliable, unchanging, constant, steadfast, dependable, resolute in his purposes, in his attributes and in what he does. He does not swerve or deviate. He does not vary. Consistent!

One of the characteristic descriptions of God is 'rock'. 'He is a rock and his ways are perfect, a God of truth, just and right is he'.[2] This description of God as a rock first appears in Exodus[3] where the Rock of Horeb was smitten 'and that Rock was Christ'.[4] So, firm, fixed, established, immovable. This is our God: 'faithful in all his ways', trustworthy.[5] He does not alter, he is immutable, devoid of all change in his being. He is always the same in his faithfulness, in his love, in his watchful care, in his generosity, in his commitment to his promises. 'God is not a man. Has he said it and will he not do it?'

Faithful too in what he has given. Once, as a child, I think I was about seven at the time, I gave my mother a birthday present. We lived then in the beautiful Northamptonshire village of Eydon. The village had two shops, one a bakery (also doubling as the Post Office); the other, surprising for such a small village, was a haberdashery run, if remember well, by two sisters called Tyrell. I bought for my mother's birthday a small table runner – all I could afford with my very limited pocket money. Indeed, in the war years family money of any sort was in short supply. However, back to that gift. If ever I was annoyed with my mother, I took the present back! Now God is not like that! He is faithful in all that he has given.

God is faithful, trustworthy, consistent, true to himself. 'The faithfulness of the Lord endures for ever'.[6] Great indeed is your faithfulness! And, this faithfulness, this consistency is firm, rock-like and despite our own faithlessness.[7] Can God ever be faithless, inconsistent? Perish the thought. Our faithlessness causes God's faithfulness to stand out in sharp relief. 'Let God be true' (to himself) which places God's veracity (akin to faithfulness) and human mendacity (the 'alley of unfaithfulness') over against one another. If we are faithless, he remains faithful, for he cannot deny himself, verses[8] that are enshrined in one of the earliest hymns of

---

2   Deuteronomy 32:4.

3   Exodus 17:6.

4   1 Corinthians 10:4.

5   Psalm 89:8; 111:7.

6   Psalm 117:2.

7   Romans 3:3, 4.

8   2 Timothy 2:11-13.

the church. No way does God keep his promises to us only if we keep our promises to him. This is unthinkable. He does not give up on us even if we fail him and muck things up. Think of Jacob!

This character of faithfulness, consistency, should be reflected too in our own lives. We too are to be committed to God's word, to his promises, to his people. We are to be 'faithful reliable people' like Moses,[9] like Paul.[10] Consistency is a fruit of the Spirit.[11] We too are to have faithful, reliable, consistent hearts.

9 Numbers 12:7.

10 1 Timothy 1:12.

11 Galatians 5:22.

D IS FOR THE DISEASED, DAMAGED HEART

'Out of the heart come....'[1]

There are a number of ways through which the performance of the heart can be impaired. These include infection by bacteria, viruses or parasites, all of which lead to a variety of inflammatory conditions. If the infection is to the outer protective covering of the heart, the pericardium, it is called pericarditis, if to the heart muscle itself it is called myocarditis and if to the inner lining of the heart chambers or the valves, it is called endocarditis. These infections ultimately lead to changes in myocardial structure in which there is damage to heart muscle cells (cardiomyopathy) and this leads to cardiac enlargement. This is due to both an increase in the number and size of existing heart muscle cells. Such cardiac enlargement makes it more difficult for the heart to pump blood around the body and this eventually leads to heart failure and death.

In my early childhood one of the most common causes of heart disease in children was as a consequence of rheumatic fever, now fortunately quite rare in the UK. This often resulted from infection by beta haemolytic streptococci, the cause of a common throat infection, especially during winter and easily spread in closed communities such as among schoolchildren. The bacteria enter the blood stream and travel to the heart resulting in secondary complications such as an acute inflammatory response affecting the heart valves (which can be life-threatening), the inner lining (endothelium) of the small blood vessels of the heart and, albeit rarely, of cardiac muscle itself. Endocarditis can also result from the increasing use of invasive dental surgery such as in preparation for implants. According to the British Cardiovascular Society the infection risk from dental surgery is 'high' and 'a big step forward' is to counteract this with prophylactic antibiotics. This significantly reduces the risk but of course, to counteract possible resistance to the antibiotic, using this approach frequently is not recommended. It is certainly important

---

1   Matthew 15:19.

to maintain good oral hygiene and have regular check-ups of teeth and gums. Viral infections commonly cause myocarditis and because this often presents with non-specific symptoms such as difficulties in breathing (dyspnoea) fatigue, exercise intolerance and palpitations it is not easy to diagnose.

A more common cause of heart muscle weakness (myocardiopathy) is that resulting from chronic alcohol consumption. While drinking one or two ounces of whisky can be shown to decrease only temporarily the efficiency of the heart, frequent repeated ingestion of alcohol in any form can lead to chronic heart muscle weakness, to cardiac failure and also to a sustained increase in blood pressure (hypertension). This has been known for some time; 'there is nothing new save that which has been forgotten'. For example, a German pathologist Otto Bollinger described in 1884 dilatation of the heart and hypertrophy among Bavarian beer drinkers. This condition became known as 'Münchener Bierherz'; at that time the average annual consumption of beer in Munich was 432 litres compared with 82 litres in other parts of Germany. It is a good idea then that the present Scottish Government has set a minimum cost for the purchase of drinks containing alcohol.

In contrast, and as W.S. Gilbert says in HMS Pinafore, 'things are seldom what they seem', a protective effect of red wine has been consistently reported. This is part of the so called 'French paradox' (partly defined as the inverse relationship between mortality from coronary heart disease and the consumption of alcohol). This protective effect, if it is real, is not due to the alcohol content of wine but to the presence, in red wine, of protective substances called antioxidants. We will think again about this in a later section.

However, the most frequent cause of cardiac damage, and indeed the leading cause of death in 'Western societies', is interference to the blood supply to the heart, as a result of narrowing and then obstruction of a major coronary artery. The extent of this damage depends upon the area of cardiac tissue supplied by an occluded artery. The reason why this is life-threatening is that, unlike the skeletal muscles in the body responsible, for example, for breathing and walking, the muscle of the heart cannot function without oxygen, that is anaerobically. The result of such an obstruction to blood flow is that after a short time, indeed just a few minutes, some heart muscle cells begin to die; the longer the blood is prevented from reaching that part of the heart the more cells will be damaged leading to cell death. The result is a myocardial infarction. If the obstruction is prolonged then damage is so severe that the heart ceases to function as a pump and death ensues. An account of attempts to reduce or save the extent of the damage is discussed later.

Now, what can cause such an obstruction to the coronary blood supply? The usual cause is the gradual build-up of fatty deposits in a major coronary artery; this is called atheroma. This restricts the blood flow to a particular part of the heart although it may not at first completely obstruct flow. However, if a blood clot (thrombus) should develop in an already partially occluded vessel then complete occlusion can occur with resulting cardiac damage and sometimes fatality.

There are two possible reasons why a complete permanent occlusion may not lead to severe damage to the heart. This is because of the possible presence of 'collateral' vessels. A simple illustration from the West of Scotland may be helpful. One of the most scenic road routes to the magnificent Scottish West coast is the A83 through Glen Croe and 'Rest and be Thankful'. Unfortunately, this major road is often closed due to rockfalls from the mountains above, for example from the Cobbler. There are two possible ways around this problem. First, the debris may be cleared manually in order to reopen the road; this often takes time especially in winter. The other option is to bypass the obstruction using an alternative route – a diversion. In the case of the A83 this can be long, a diversion of over fifty miles for those that live beyond the blockage, the residents of Inveraray for example. Another possibility, being presently considered, is to reopen the old cattle drover's narrow road in the valley below.

Now let us return to the heart situation of a closed, or partially closed, coronary artery. The above two possible options concerning the A83 also apply to an obstructed coronary artery. The debris can be cleared to reopen the artery by a relatively simple operation (once the hospital has been reached) using an instrument to dislodge the debris contributing to the offending obstruction and/or to administer a 'clot busting' drug. But, how about the other means of supplying blood to the affected part, which we illustrated above as a 'diversion'? In some, perhaps many, cases such a 'diversion' is already in place. These are vessels originating from another coronary artery, or from a branch of the occluded artery arising above (proximal to) that obstruction. Such vessels, termed 'collateral vessels' can be seen at post-mortem especially in the hearts of older people. It has been estimated that about 25% of patients without a relevant coronary stenosis have such preformed collaterals; even more are present in those with coronary artery disease. There is a wonderful demonstration of this in a book by the late Dr William (Bill) Fulton written as a result of studies undertaken over many years when he was a consultant cardiologist at Stobhill Hospital in Glasgow. This is one of the few books that also provides a viewer (tucked in a pocket at the rear of the book) in order to see, in three dimensions, such collateral coronary vessels. How these protective new diversion channels arise, the result of a fascinating process called arteriogenesis, is discussed later in the book.

Now, how does this description of the diseased, damaged physical heart, the organ responsible for pumping blood around the whole body relate, if at all, to our spiritual heart, the 'inner man'? Scripture often refers to the diseased or damaged heart, a kind of spiritual myocarditis. In his explanation of the parable about what defiles a person,[2] Jesus said it is 'out of the heart' come things that defile a person; he listed these – evil thoughts, murder, adultery, sexual immorality, theft, false witness, slander. The inner man, says Jesus, is polluted, 'made filthy', and is 'desperately sick'; the heart is also described as 'desperately wicked'.[3]

In all our hearts then there is a viral infection, an 'evil disease'[4] and this infection defiles.[5] Scripture calls this 'sin'. The hub, the core of this, is self-interest, that fundamental desire to serve one's own ends; we become 'puffed up' with our own importance and pride.[6] Further, it is 'lifted up' against God,[7] it sits in God's place. Every human heart, said Jesus, is like a storehouse. What comes out of it depends on what is within; the seed of every sin is embedded in every human heart: and this leads to general body dysfunction. The human heart then is a reservoir that spills its contents out in every bodily activity; 'in some decaying room lurks that impurity that cannot be contained and which, like some feebly concealed and poisoned waste, escapes to corrupt the whole'. So, the seed of every sin is embedded

---

2   Matthew 15:10-20.

3   Jeremiah 17:9.

4   Ecclesiastes 6:2 AV (other versions do not use the word disease).

5   Titus 1:15.

6   Colossians 2:18.

7   Ezekiel 28:2.

in every human heart; it is 'graven' (stamped upon) the 'table of the heart'[8] written with a pen of iron or the point of a diamond. It is impossible to erase as the heart itself gets harder and more resistant to God and his word. So, Scripture piles up the descriptions of the state of the human heart. Diseased, damaged indeed. Further, this disease is 'beyond cure',[9] 'pain perpetual and wound incurable' because it refuses to be healed.[10] 'Your sins have increased and there are no medicines for your wound',[11] no healing for the diseased, damaged human heart. And, as with the diseased physical heart, the spiritual heart cannot function as it should. Disease leads to damage and, as Paul argues in his letter to the church in Rome, the end result is spiritual death.[12]

Perhaps, clearest of all to see (this self-interest and the desire to serve one's own ends) comes in the account of the trials and crucifixion of Jesus Christ.[13] The easy way out taken by Pilate, wanting to do one thing, not taking a decision he knew to be right, spurning the anguished pleading of his wife ('have nothing to do with that righteous man') but ending up doing the other thing, condemning one he knew in his heart to be innocent, simply washing his hands of a difficult situation. Then there is the closed mind, the entrenched intransigence of religious belief, of Caiaphas, and the cruelty of the soldiers, excusing themselves (because they were just following orders) then playing at the foot of the cross, jeering, pouring scorn on the one hanging above them. And what of the disciples themselves? Peter, the threefold lies to save his own skin, the others nowhere to be seen when the chips were down, their courage haemorrhaging away, the later doubts of Thomas despite the clear testimony of his friends. Surely these are reflections of our own actions. We have all been there, hungering for recognition, playing safe, promising much and delivering little. 'Were you there when they crucified my Lord?'

It is here that we come to the central tenet of the Christian faith. This is that there is a cure for spiritual heart disease, that was once 'wound incurable' with 'no medicine'. The Christian response is that there is healing for that diseased heart. Jesus came into the world to save his people from

---

8 Jeremiah 17:1.
9 Jeremiah 30:12, 15.
10 Jeremiah 15:18.
11 Jeremiah 30:13.
12 Romans 5:12.
13 Matthew 26:56-75 and 27:11-26.

their sin,[14] indeed 'to save sinners'.[15] For we are all such, we are all in the same boat; 'all (without exception) have sinned and fallen short of the glory of God'.[16] It is to the whole universal psyche that severe damage has taken place. That is, we have all failed to fulfil the purpose for which we were brought into the world. And, it is while we were in this state, 'yet sinners' that, because of God's love for mankind, Christ died on the Cross for us.[17] Our sins, like Paul's[18] were 'washed away'. Salvation became available! (See the chapter on P for protection).

---

14 Matthew 1:21.

15 1 Timothy 1:15.

16 Romans 3:22, 23.

17 Romans 5:8.

18 Acts 22:16.

E is for the EXERCISED HEART

*'Christian exercises, however good in themselves
are not the goal of our Christian life,
although they are the necessary means of its attainment'.*

Exercise is primarily physical activity in order to gain strength and vigour and to keep healthy. And, over my lifetime we are, as a people, getting less active. Gone are the days when we worked physically to such an extent in farms, factories or even in the home. This decrease in heavy physical activity at work has come in part as the result of the invention of cars, computers, television, home cinemas, the internet and the rise of labour-saving devices. Mechanised modern life has led to less and less energy expenditure by almost all classes of people. We work more from home, avoiding the effort involved in traveling to work. Good for some. But as a consequence, we are physically slowly grinding to a halt! And it starts early; only 11% of Scottish children aged 10 and 11 take at least an hour of vigorous exercise daily and the average member of this age group is sedentary for seven and a half hours a day. There is a price to pay for this general lack of fitness; we are being killed by inactivity and this contributes to the rise in cardiovascular disease, in obesity and in diabetes.

Getting your body moving is one of the most important ways to improve the health of your heart. Indeed, it is claimed that being physically active can reduce the risk of heart and other circulatory diseases by as much as 35%, by mechanisms still as yet to be clearly defined. Certainly, there is good evidence that people with a physically active job have fewer heart attacks than those in more sedentary occupations. For example, in a study published in the medical journal 'Lancet' in 1966, J.N. Morris (and others) examined the health records of almost 18,000 British civil servants with sedentary desk jobs and found that those who, in their leisure time, were more active (running, hiking, playing team games) had an incidence of coronary artery disease one-half of the workers who were less active. Important news perhaps for those civil servants, politicians too maybe, presently active in any form of time consuming negotiations.

One of the first, and for this author still one of the most convincing, pieces of evidence for the protective effects of exercise was an historical study of bus workers in London published, also in the Lancet and again by Morris and co-workers, in 1953. In those far off days there were always two people 'on the buses'; the driver (always male) and the (usually) female conductor or 'clippie'. The latter, on their feet all day, were responsible for the collection of the fares, giving out tickets and clipping them to make sure they were not reused. Almost all the buses at that time were double-deckers so that the 'clippie' had to run up and down stairs, a vigorous form of exercise that was both regular and strenuous. This was in marked contrast to the driver, who was simply sitting busy keeping his eyes on the road and occasionally moving his feet to change gear. In this trial of the incidence, or severity, of heart disease in these two populations, the striking finding was that it was far less in the active bus conductors, the clippies, than in the more sedentary drivers. There are of course complicating factors in this study: the drivers were all men and the conductors were nearly all women. As we will see gender is an independent factor for cardiovascular disease; women of childbearing age are less susceptible to cardiac disease than are men of the same age. And, how much did smoking contribute?

The important questions are: how does this protection work, and how much exercise is required to keep the heart, and the rest of the body, healthy. An associated question is whether physical inactivity is really a risk factor for heart disease. These questions are not easy to answer. First, we consider the beneficial effects of regular exercise.

As far as the heart is concerned exercise results in an increase in respiration and heart rate (tachycardia); even when just standing and then walking gently around the home, the heart rate increase is appreciable. The higher the intensity of the exercise the greater the increase in heart rate. For example, during the 2019 University boat race on the Thames, when the heart rates of the participants, all young and well trained, were continuously recorded (I think for the first time), the rate of one of the women crew members rose to 209 beats/minute whilst that of the oldest male participant (aged forty-six!) increased, during a particularly crucial stage of the race, to 196 beats/minute. A rush of adrenaline! However, the usual, and safe maximum heart rate during exercise is reckoned to be approximately 220 beats/minute minus your age. If you are 85 for example then that would be 135 beats/minute, about twice your resting heart rate.

With this tachycardia there is an increase in the amount of blood ejected by the heart at each beat, the stroke volume, and the total cardiac output might be increased by up to five times from about 5 litres/minute to 25 litres/minute. This could be far higher in trained athletes. With this increase in the output of the heart, blood flow is markedly increased, particularly to the exercising muscles and especially if it is the legs that are involved. This increase in muscle blood flow is due to the dilatation of the vessels running through these muscles, and this includes the muscle of the heart; at the same time, there is a corresponding decrease in blood flow to those parts of the body such as the gut and the kidneys that perform tasks not pertinent to exercise. This means that there a redistribution of blood flow within the body. This is one of the many marvels of the human circulation. There is one other consequence of this flow increase to the active muscles. This is that the uptake of oxygen (and glucose) from the blood to the tissues is also increased perhaps by as much as threefold.

Apart from reducing the risk of premature death from heart disease, there are other beneficial effects of exercise, provided it is regular. These include helping to control body weight, a reduced risk of type 2 diabetes, a better lipid profile: that 'switch' from bad lipids (low density lipoprotein) to good lipids (high density lipoprotein). There could also be an improvement in brain function; an increase in the growth of new neurons in the hippocampus (which is that part of the brain concerned with memory retention) and a reduction in the degeneration of existing neurons. Some studies have shown a reduction in the number of 'poor mental health days' by as much as 20%: 'exercise is associated with a lower mental health burden across people no matter their age, gender, race, income or level of education'.

The next important question concerns what kind of exercise is best for these protective effects and how much of it is needed. As to the kind of exercise, it is clear that aerobic (isotonic) exercise, which means that muscles involved sustain their oxygen supply throughout, is best because the shortening and relaxation of the active muscles (which involve movement, rhythmically tensing and relaxing) requires more oxygen – and hence more blood flow and a greater cardiac output. Anaerobic (isometric) exercise, where the muscles stay at approximately the same length throughout, such as in lifting or holding, seems to be less protective, in part because such activities 'squeeze' the blood out of the muscles.

What kind of aerobic exercise is suitable? It does not mean necessarily going to the gym. It simply means moving around. Walking, taking the stairs rather than the lift, swimming, cycling, skipping, gardening. Routine housework even, one hour of which burns 250 calories. Regular brisk walking, particularly at a rate sufficient to increase respiration and heart rate, making us sweat and slightly breathless, is a form of exercise most of us can do and for which we are wonderfully structured and adapted, moving as we do by bipedal progression. Brisk walking is as beneficial as running, and less strain on the knees, especially on hard surfaces; running for three miles is no more beneficial than briskly walking the same distance. The important point is that such walking should ideally be brisk (about 3.4 miles per hour or a 'mile every twenty minutes'), no 'ambling', enough exertion to make you slightly breathless.

It is important too not to neglect muscle strength and balance. But, how far and how often? Public Health England say even 10,000 steps a day is not enough. The usual figure given is 20 to 30 minutes activity a day, not necessarily all at the same time, that is 'in divided doses', or 150 minutes a week in small bouts of 10 minutes or more daily. For older folk this may not be always possible and, if the weather is inclement, walking up and down stairs inside the house for those ten minutes is just as good. Indeed, fifteen minutes spent climbing stairs consumes as much energy as the same amount of time spent cycling. Possibly! What is important is that this exercise is regular, daily if possible. Keep moving.

We do not know how long this protection of the heart afforded by exercise lasts; suppose, for example, one stops exercising for a time, how soon is this protection lost – if at all? In our own experimental studies daily exercise (or increasing heart rate by some other means such as pacing induced tachycardia) is capable of keeping the heart protected for a long time, several days after the exercise has stopped. However, of course, if one was incapacitated for a time, hospitalised for example, then it is likely that exercise-induced heart protection is probably lost and needs to be regained by building up a regular exercise routine. But slowly! This is an area for further clinical research – how much and how long? Still open questions and not easy to answer because there are too many other variables.

How does the above relate to spiritual exercise? The ability to maintain and improve the health of our spiritual hearts and protect them from damage and spiritual disease?

Some time ago I heard on BBC radio 4 a recording of a Sunday morning service from St Martin-in-the-Fields in Trafalgar Square, London. The speaker was Reverend Richard Carter of the Nazareth Community at the church. He spoked about spiritual disciplines or exercises. These were easy to remember (even for me) because all his seven points began with the same letter – S.

- Silence (creating times for God to speak),
- Signs (of God in nature and especially about trees, as in Psalm 1 - deep roots, timeless),
- Seasons (God's seasons of life, how one season follows another, illustrating God's consistency and faithfulness),
- Service (Christ has no body on earth except our own, no feet to go, no hands to do, we all have something to give),
- Supplication (praying for others),
- Scripture (God speaking, meditating, meaning, 'eat the scroll', the many flavours of God's word)
- Sacrament (Christ remembered, Christ present, Christ sending – 'our lives become his gospel').

Helpful. At least to me.

I asked my eldest son Stephen, active in 'spiritual accompanying' to contribute what he felt about spiritual exercises. I abstract (full text available from Stephen at steve.parratt@gmail.com) in what follows.

Just as physical exercise is good for the overall health of the body, improving circulation, muscle tone, breathing, so too spiritual exercise is good for the spiritual life, increasing a God-given openness to the Holy Spirit. They are not an end in themselves but rather enable us to respond more faithfully to the love of God, setting us free to become more and more the person God intended us to be.[1] Anything that helps us become more open to God and his love, drawing us into a deeper relationship and friendship with God is a spiritual exercise, which are neither mysterious nor mystical. Stephen quotes Jan Johnson and her helpful image of sailing and rowing; in rowing (see above!) all the effort in getting somewhere is up to the rowers themselves, no matter how experienced and strong they are they cannot keep going indefinitely, whereas in sailing the effort is to get the boat

1   Galatians 5:1, 13, 14.

in the right place to 'catch the wind'. So, it is with spiritual exercises; these are to get us into the right place to catch the wind of the Spirit in our sails – connecting with God.

So, what are these exercises? Some were outlined above in the S series. They include prayer (confession), fasting, the study of God's word (the so-called 'inward disciplines') and the corporate exercises of worship, celebration and communion, service. To these I would add this. As with physical exercise we need help, akin to a 'personal trainer', in this case God himself by his Spirit.

Some, including me, have here found Leslie Weatherhead's book *A Private House of Prayer* helpful.[2] In it he pictures an internal journey into six rooms of a house through which he moves one by one as a help to wandering minds! It begins (room 1) with the realisation that God is with us, the Divine presence.[3] We then move to room 2 (adoration, praise, thanksgiving), to confession, forgiveness and 'unloading' (room 3), reception and petition (for oneself in rooms 4 and 5), intercession (for others, room 6) then meditating on God's word (room 7 but perhaps this should be room 1!). The important thing is that any spiritual exercise is between you and the Lord; one to one, surely the key to spiritual growth. I note that such 'one to ones' with Jesus are common in John's gospel (Mary, Nicodemus, Thomas, Peter) even though sometimes others were present. So, for spiritual exercise one to one with the open Bible. No substitute. Exercise in a chair or on your knees. The key to a healthy heart.

---

2 First published in 1958 by Hodder and Stoughton and revised in 1999. Sadly, as with so many good books, out of print. Well worth searching for!

3 As, for example, in Psalm 46: 1, 7, 11.

F is for the FAILING HEART

'My heart may fail but God is the strength of my heart.'[1]

'Has his steadfast love ever failed?'
'The steadfast love of the Lord never fails.'[2]

*'Provide yourselves with a treasure in the heavens
that does not fail.'*[3]

Pumps of any kind can fail. Failure of the one controlling your central heating or that petrol pump in the car can be annoying and disconcerting but is rarely terminal. Each pump can be replaced. Failure of your pumping heart is a different matter altogether. Heart (circulatory) failure can be, and eventually will be, the end of life. Further, the number of people living with heart failure in increasing. This is due, in part, to the fact that we live longer. Thus, the incidence is about 2% at the age of fifty but is over 10% at age eighty. One reason why this figure is not much higher is improvements in acute treatment, and thus survival, from major cardiovascular events such as myocardial infarction. Overall, cardiac (and respiratory) disease leading to cardiac failure is a major contributor to the global burden of disease. The mortality is 10 to 40%. Almost half of the patients affected die within five years of the initial diagnosis.

Heart failure occurs when there is an inability of the heart to pump blood efficiently. This means that there is an inadequate blood flow to meet the needs of the tissues of the body. The heart is not functioning as it should; it is failing to deliver what the cells of the body need, the oxygen and nutrients required for normal cellular function. It means that the amount of blood ejected by the heart at each beat (called stroke volume) is reduced and more blood is left in the heart after contraction; normally the heart ejects about 60 – 70% of the blood it receives, in cardiac failure this may be a little as 40%.

---

1   Psalm 73:26.

2   Psalm 77:8; Lamentations 3:22.

3   Luke 12:33.

The symptoms include shortness of breath, even during normal routine activity, swelling of the lower extremities (ankles and feet) and fatigue, a feeling of being unusually tired and weak – 'a weary tiredness, everything is an effort'. The reason for this is that blood flow to skeletal muscle is insufficient. This failure of the heart can be detected by a chest X-ray, by an electrocardiogram and echocardiogram and also by the measurement in the blood of certain enzymes.

Put very simply this can be failure of one side of the heart, left or right. Certainly, it can begin this way. It can be described as forward or backward failure. A simple illustration might help. Hopefully! Consider a visit to the supermarket. You have collected all you need and are queuing up at the check-out desk to pay. Frustratingly, ahead of the queue you have chosen to join there is at the checkout a new, inexperienced person waiting to serve you and take your payment. Cheerful but slow. Compared to the experienced colleague at the next check-out desk, the number of satisfied (?) customers leaving your checkout having paid, is reduced (forward failure) and there is a backlog of none too happy customers still waiting behind you to pay (backward failure). A very simple picture as to what happens in 'forward' and 'backward' cardiac failure.

Let us think first of the possible consequences of forward failure when it occurs in the left ventricle, remembering that this pumps blood into the general (systemic) circulation. This reduced output, and an initial blood pressure reduction, would result in a decreased blood flow to the peripheral tissues of the body; not enough blood is reaching them to meet their needs. This is compensated by attempts to maintain arterial pressure by constriction of the blood vessels, resulting from increased discharge down the sympathetic nerves. This reduction in tissue blood flow can be seen most clearly in the kidneys (reduced urinary output) and in skeletal muscle, where it leads to muscle weakness, tiredness and hence difficulties in the ability to exercise. Indeed, this means that the typical heart failure patient will become accustomed to an inexorable decline in physical vigour and performance, running is no longer possible, climbing stairs, even walking (especially when carrying loads) become difficult if not impossible.

Secondly, we think of the consequences of 'backward' failure. The build-up of pressure behind the left ventricle leads to increases in the left atrial pressure and to general pulmonary venous congestion. The result is difficulty in breathing (dyspnoea) especially when lying down. This is relieved somewhat by sitting; (the word orthopnoea simply means difficulty in breathing except in the upright position).

In contrast, if there is a failure on the right side of the heart the most significant feature is the result of 'backward' failure behind the right ventricle; generalised systemic venous congestion with distended veins, most evident in the jugular veins in the neck together with oedema, loss of fluid into 'soft' tissues such as the liver, the gastrointestinal tract and the lower limbs, the legs and the feet. The most recognisable feature in such waterlogged patients is cyanosis especially in the toes and feet due, in part, to the external fluid exerting pressure on the thin walled veins.

Heart failure occurs when the heart is diseased or when excessive demands are placed upon it. Usually it is a gradual process which can be categorised according to that suggested many years ago by the New York Heart Association. Thus, limitation of severe activity, but not under resting conditions, is Grade II, limitation of activity on mild exertion is Grade III and most seriously, limitation of activity at rest, restricting the patient to a chair or bed is Grade IV. The features here are breathlessness especially when lying flat as when sleeping; this improves on sitting up. The reason for this is the redistribution of fluid from the periphery to the low-pressure pulmonary circulation. There is a general distension of veins, especially of the lower limbs and of the liver. Compensatory mechanisms take place to attempt to counteract these effects. These include an increase in heart rate (tachycardia). For those wondering about Grade I on the NYHA scale don't worry! This involves hardly any limitation of the patient's physical activity and no symptoms either at rest or during normal activity.

So, what are the causes? Narrowing of the coronary arteries leading to necrosis – meaning the pathological death of cells many of which are still in contact with living tissue. Even small areas of cellular damage can result in pump failure. This is due to regional contractile dysfunction. Especially insidious factors include an elevated arterial blood pressure. Hypertension invariably leads to heart failure because the heart then has to eject blood against an increased load; the heart has to work harder in order to force blood into the arteries. There is an increase in resistance, defined by the pressure flow relationship; pressure is increased but flow is decreased. Think of the effort involved in attempting to push heavy furniture around compared with moving a light dining room chair. Other causes of heart failure include some defect in the ability of cardiac cells to metabolise adequately as in diabetes, or some structural abnormality resulting from excessive alcohol ingestion.

Early drug intervention is important in order to prevent progression of the disease. This is outside the present scope although it is significant that attempted therapy in a bygone age with digitalis alkaloids, standard therapy when I was a student several decades ago, now gets little mention except in some patients when it is given to relieve severe symptoms although not to prolong life. Such drugs, derived from the common foxglove (digitalis), certainly increase the ability of the heart to contract. Indeed, William Withering wrote (in 1775) that 'foxglove has a power over the motion of the heart to a degree yet unobserved in any other medicine'. However, this 'power' comes at the expense of excessive oxygen demand. Better rather to reduce the physical demands upon the failing heart by decreasing arterial blood pressure and/or by slowing the heart.

Failure can be defined, as in the Oxford dictionary, as inadequate, lacking, feeble, or imperfect. It also means to 'fall short' or to be 'at fault'. This is the meaning in Scripture. Not surprisingly, the word comes often, 'my heart failed within me' or, as in David's word to King Saul before his fight with the Philistine champion Goliath, 'let no man's heart fail because of him'.[4] These are examples of fearfulness, a failure of courage. However, there are other biblical causes of 'failure'. Sometimes the reference is to more than bodily, physical failure. For David this occurred when his own heart failed him, when his inner resources were eroded through his failing health ('my strength fails, my bones are consumed')[5], although there is some debate as to the translation of this particular verse. Is this failure because of some physical affliction ('misery', 'affliction' in the RSV and NIV) or of sinfulness in his life ('iniquity' as in the AV and ESB; 'my wrongs' as in Greenberg, 'guilt' in the NIV margin). Certainly, whatever the circumstances of this psalm, David's life was in turmoil and all the symptoms of spiritual heart failure are here apparent.

We need to look more closely at both this psalm (and also Psalm 38) to understand what characterises spiritual heart failure. These are psalms for the darkest of days. The key phrases are 'my heart pants' (palpitates, throbs)

---

4   1 Samuel 17:32.
5   Psalm 31:10.

and 'my strength (heart) fails'.[6] Is this solely physical, indeed is this cardiac failure, heart discomfort? Is the psalmist struggling with severe illness, wounds festering, no 'soundness in his flesh', strength failing, a heart in pain? Or is it his failing spiritual heart resulting from the sickness of sin? David, the author of these psalms was clearly going through a hard time. The circumstances are unclear but probably relate to the time when fleeing for his life from King Saul, who had a murderous intent on his life. And this after a period when life for David all was going so well – musician to the king. If so then this was failure partly through fear, fear for his life, because he was 'on the run'. One wonders if this was a single experience; probably it was because one could hardly accuse David of physical cowardice.

The background of Psalm 38, one of the penitential psalms, is again uncertain but what is certainly clear is that it was again a cry from David in his darkest days. Certainly, here the problem was his sin, he was 'beset', marred by sin. He is bringing into his mind the remembrance of past (and present?) sin, as it states in the heading to this psalm. The sickness of the body accompanies the sickness of the soul. His heart is failing; high on the NYHA scale. He is near the end of his tether; there is a deep consciousness of sin ('no rest because of my sin'; 'my iniquities have gone over my head'). His problem here is that of 'foolishness', of sin. It becomes too heavy for him, he is troubled, bowed down greatly, prostrate, feeble; there is 'disquietness of heart', his heart 'pants', 'throbs', akin perhaps to the tachycardia that is often seen in heart failure patients. He is discomforted, 'numb, utterly crushed, alone', 'I roar from the ache (tumult) in my heart' (v. 8 in the Greenberg translation) 'my heart goes around like a beggar'. Certainly, Grade IV in any spiritual NYHA classification!

There is an interesting perspective on this psalm in the Africa Bible Commentary. The author suggests that this psalm 'could be prayed by many who suffer in Africa from HIV/AIDS, especially those infected by a spouse or by a blood transfusion'. They are suffering physical wasting ('no soundness in my flesh, my wounds stink') and are the scorn of friends and neighbours. Of course, this is not to imply that physical suffering is always a consequence of sin, an error Job's friends made. Jesus[7] is clear on this, but it does happen that suffering is the result of people's wrongdoing or

---

6   Psalm 38:10.

7   John 9:1-5.

foolishness and the psalmist here does draw this parallel, 'my foolishness',[8] 'I confess my iniquity, I am sorry for my sin', it is 'because of my iniquity that my strength fails and my bones waste away'.[9] Certainly, sickness of body can accompany sickness of soul.

What can be done about this throbbing, tumultuous, failing heart? A good physician is needed! And, who better than God himself? So, the psalmist turns to prayer 'make haste to help me',[10] 'be gracious to me O Lord'[11] 'make your face to shine upon your servant' and then ultimately to praise, 'blessed be the Lord'.[12]

The present therapy of physical cardiac failure is to 'unload' the heart by slowing it and reducing the pressure against which it pumps blood. The equivalent in spiritual heart failure is a similar; 'unloading' by confession and by trust. We are to 'be strong, let the heart take courage and wait on the Lord'.[13]

---

8 Psalm 38:5.

9 Psalm 31:10.

10 Psalm 38:22.

11 Psalm 31:9.

12 Psalm 31:21.

13 Psalm 31:24.

G is for the GENEROUS HEART

'God gives to all mankind life and breath and all things.'[1]

'Every good gift is.... from the Father.'[2]

Sixty years ago, and by a somewhat circuitous route from West Africa, my wife and I visited the land where the feet of Jesus had once trod. The lovely quietness of Galilee, Capernaum, where we were so generously welcomed by the resident French priest, Jerusalem and, for a day trip, the Dead Sea. We have photos of us sitting in the water reading a newspaper to prove it. The journey by taxi was 'through the wilderness', where on route the driver was too frightened to stop to enable a photograph to be taken because of possible robbers and bandits. A reminder of the possible dangers the pilgrims of old faced as they went up to Jerusalem for the annual feasts outlined in Psalms 120–134, the 'Songs of Ascents' and the reason for that question of the psalmist 'I lift up my eyes to the hills. From whence does my help come?'[3] Why did he particularly need that help 'in the hills'? Perhaps because of the presence there of similar robbers and bandits.

The Dead Sea was, in those days, really a place of death, little or nothing living in its waters. Why? Because although there in an inlet from the Jordan river, there is little or no outlet. All that it receives is retained. Keeping but not giving out. No life, because living comes from giving as well as receiving. As the Lord says, 'it is more blessed to give than to receive'.[4]

If this was not true of the beating human heart then indeed there would be no life. It is difficult to imagine a heart that receives and retains blood and does not then give it out again into the circulation. It would be a dead heart indeed. Our living heart takes in and then gives out.

Of course, it is true that not all the blood received by the ventricles is ejected, pumped out into the circulation. There is always a proportion that

---

1   Acts 17:25.

2   James 1:17.

3   Psalm 121:1.

4   Acts 20:35.

is retained, left in the ventricle after the completion of contraction. The amount left in the heart at the end of each systole is called the end-systolic or residual volume (ESV) which is less in women than in men. Female hearts then are more generous since less is retained! So, most of the blood within the heart (about 70%) has been ejected. When the ability of the heart to contract is impaired then the amount of blood left in the heart after contraction is much increased; the heart is 'failing', unable to give out.

During exercise ESV is initially increased; this is part of what is known as the 'Starling effect' which states that the output (the stroke volume) is dependent upon the volume of blood in the ventricle at the beginning of the contraction process. ESV then decreases as the contractile force is increased, due to the presence of higher circulation catecholamine levels. This means that output is modified by two independent but related properties of the myocardium: first, the ability of the ventricle to fill, which involves the relaxing properties of the heart, its distensibility; second, the ability of the heart to empty, or partially empty which depends on the ability of the heart to contract – and therefore the function of the contractile properties and efficiency of the ventricles. In physiological terms then the output of the heart depends upon the amount of blood in the heart before contraction begins, the ability of the heart muscle to contract (called contractility), the heart rate and the resistance (blood pressure) against which the heart pumps.

At this point it might be helpful to remember that the heart beats about 100,000 times a day and that the ventricles daily 'move' over this period around 8,000 litres into the vascular tree. This is because at each beat the output (called the stroke volume) is about 70 to 90ml/beat, that is about 5 to 6 litres per minute. Exercise may increase this temporarily by from five to six times due to an increase in both stroke volume and in heart rate. Time now for a fresh calculation! One other fact to bear in mind is that the total amount of blood in a human body weighing 70kg is also from 5 to 6 litres. This is about 1/14th (or 8%) of total body weight, meaning that the heart at rest pumps into the circulation the equivalent of its total blood volume, all the blood in the body, each minute! Imagine! What a generous heart we have!

We should next think about the fluid, the blood, that is pumped around the body. Blood has been described as 'that truly remarkable juice', the 'vital fluid', a 'precious deposit'. William Harvey, the discoverer of the circulation, wrote 'blood is the cause of life in general, the first to live and the last to die'. Blood is a warm, sticky, soup-like suspension of cells, red blood cells (erythrocytes), white cells (the soldiers of the circulation). With platelets together these cells make up about half of the total blood volume. These are contained in a watery solution, the plasma.

Blood can be lost or given. Lost when a blood vessel is severed, or during menstruation when about 50ml is lost each month, equivalent to about twenty teaspoonfuls. Women during the reproductive period thus lose about 20 litres of blood, 4 times their total blood volume. Usually however blood does not leave the body; it is confined to the blood vessels. When it does leave the body and, is persistent (haemorrhage) it can be serious, even life-threatening. It needs to be prevented; by tourniquet, suture, clamp or pressure from a thumb. Everyone has one! The persistent appearance of blood out of the blood vessels, for example in the urine, faeces or phlegm indicates that something potentially serious is happening within the body.

However, blood can also be given by those generous enough to do so, for it is life-saving. Blood transfusion has an interesting history. It was first attempted in France when Jean-Baptiste Denis (of the Academie des Sciences in Paris) transfused lamb's blood into a human – with fatal results. Not surprising. After then being banned for 150 years the procedure of transfusion was reintroduced in London in 1818 by an obstetrician, James Blundell. He stipulated two things; first that it should only be attempted in women near to death following severe blood loss through uterine haemorrhage and second, that only human blood should be used. As one might predict only some attempted transfusions were successful; it was fortunate that in such cases the blood grouping must have been appropriate. There was also a shortage of donors! Transfusions are now of course essential for patients with excessive blood loss and although there is still a shortage of blood donors, they are presently compensated; with every 500ml (roughly a pint) donated, which is roughly the equivalent of that lost in menstruation each year, one is 'given' a cup of tea and a biscuit. The blood is then sold to hospitals at a price of about £250 a litre! That would buy quite a lot of biscuits. The important thing is that this 'remarkable juice' is given by a donor and then provided, also 'freely' given, to the needy patient.

What is it that makes blood so remarkable? What does it do within the body? What is its function and why is it so important? There are three answers to these questions. First, it is nutritive; it provides so generously all that the individual body cells require to function. It is life giving. The key constituent here are the red blood cells, the erythrocytes. There are about 5 million of these cells in each cubic ml of blood and each, in their short lifespan (about three months) travels about 100 miles. This journey includes buffeting in the chambers of the heart, the change in shape as they squeeze through the narrowest of blood vessels and the huge energy requirements needed for the exchange, the transfer, of oxygen from the haemoglobin within them into the cells. The recent account of the rescue of the young Thai football team from a flooded underground cave illustrates this; in the final stage of the rescue each team member had to carry, through the narrowest of passages, his own oxygen. And, all under water. Like red blood cells in the watery suspension of plasma 'carrying' its oxygen through the narrowest of the smallest blood vessels, the capillaries.

Blood has a second essential function; it carries away the rubbish produced by each cell, the waste products of metabolism that would poison the cell if left. Third, blood has a cellular protective, defensive function; if a blood vessel is damaged with the possibility of blood loss then the clotting mechanisms come into play to prevent the loss of this remarkable life-giving juice.

The spiritual implications of these three functions of blood have been detailed previously.[5] In summary, we receive, have been given, spiritual life through the blood of Jesus. Just as each cell in our body receives all that is needed for physical life, pumped by our generous hearts, so too spiritual life comes through the flowing blood of Jesus on the Cross, so generously, freely given.

The 'generosity' of the heart in giving out is, as we have seen, incomplete; at each beat only about 70% of the life-giving blood contained within the heart is given out into the body. However, the generosity of God is lavish. He is the freely giving God. He hands over to us, transfers to us, and freely, his gifts; and, they are given to all who are willing to accept them. He gives to all 'life and breath and all things'.[6] These are 'good gifts',[7] indeed 'perfect gifts' because they come from God the Father.[8] The Bible tells us these include food, light, peace, understanding, wisdom, strength, grace and life itself. Good gifts indeed! Yet above all these God has given the greatest gift of all,

---

5 Jim Parratt, *Marvellously Made*, Handsel Press, 2017.

6 Acts 17:25.

7 Matthew 7:11.

8 James 1:17.

the supreme, the 'unspeakable' gift of his only Son, Jesus[9] to be received as a gift 'by grace through faith'.[10] And, even more generously, there comes with the gift of Jesus the gift of eternal, resurrection life, the life inherent in God himself.[11] It is for those who have first been 'given' by the Father to the Son.[12] Then there is the wonderful gift of the Holy Spirit, the Comforter, the Spirit of Truth who comes alongside to help and sustain. He is the one whom Jesus promised, the one prayed for to the Father and who was given so lavishly, so generously to the church at Pentecost. For us, he comes in response to asking[13] and is received by faith.[14]

However, being grateful recipients of this generosity has implications for our own giving. Having received so much from our so generous God, we too are to be generous givers – 'the righteous gives and does not hold back'.[15] This generous giving comes from joyful,[16] blest hearts.[17] To be generous is to be hospitable,[18] it 'opens the door to the sojourner'[19] as Abraham did to the angels, as Reuel did to Moses and as the old man of Ephraim did to the Levite.[20] Generosity then is one of the marks of a genuine Christian life. There is a delightful example of this kind of abundant giving in the account of the project to build the Temple.[21] David and the leaders under him invested their own resources in the building, they served and gave generously yet crucially also acknowledged that these resources had first of all been given to them by God, the Creator, Owner and Giver of all,[22] 'all this abundance that we have provided comes from your hand and is all your own'. What a generous God!

---

9 John 3:16; 4:10.
10 Ephesians 2:8.
11 John 10:28; Romans 6:23.
12 John 10:29.
13 Luke 11:13.
14 Galatians 3:14.
15 Proverbs 21:26.
16 2 Corinthians 8:2.
17 Acts 20:35.
18 Hebrews 13:2.
19 Job 31:32.
20 Judges 19:16-21.
21 1 Chronicles 29:1-5.
22 1 Chronicles 29:10-16.

H is for HOT AND COLD HEARTS

'My heart was hot within me.'[1]
'Did not our hearts burn within us?'[2]

We are warm hearted creatures! Our hearts, like the rest of our bodies, function best at an optimum temperature of 37 degrees. We do not, like frogs and toads, simply take on the temperature of our surroundings. We do not, intentionally at any rate, hibernate. This is defined as a 'state of torpor' (numbness, dullness, indifference). The common toad which, buried since autumn, when coming out from underground shelters, heralds like daffodils and swallows, the coming of Spring.

This hibernation is essentially a specialised form of adaptive, seasonal hypothermia. There is a marked reduction in body temperature, a slowing of metabolism and a profound decrease in heart rate. For example, in hedgehogs the heart rate may fall from 190 to 20 beats a minute; in black bears the heart rate during hibernation may be as low as 8 beats a minute. There is an interesting story about black bears. A biologist, brave and dedicated, entered their den and attempted to listen to the heartbeat of the hibernating bear. Undetectable. With gentle prodding there was a discernible pulse. A few minutes later the bear raised its head and in five minutes the heart rate (of the bear and of the biologist!) had soared to 175 beats a minute. Time for a rapid exit!

There is a condition of the heart, first described in 1985, that is sometimes referred to as the 'hibernating myocardium'. This happens when there is a persisting limitation of coronary blood flow over a prolonged period, months or even years and, in some patients, indefinitely. The heart remains viable (demonstrated by cardiac imaging techniques) but the ability to contract is impaired; the heart has, in effect, 'gone to sleep'. In most subjects this is usually reversible after restoration of coronary blood flow.

---

1   Psalm 39:3.
2   Luke 24:32.

Whether hibernating (or even 'stunning') are adequate terms to describe this form of heart malfunction is debateable but there are certainly situations when 'cold is good' for the heart. Hearts for transplants are kept in a cool box, sometimes also oxygenated, because the low temperature reduces energy requirements. Bigelow in Toronto in the early 1950's had showed that even moderate hypothermia (25 to 28 degrees) protects the heart against injury through this mechanism. More recent studies have shown that even relatively small reductions in temperature (down to just 35 degrees) can also protect the myocardium; this is partly due to the decrease in heart rate.

There was an interesting case recently from near Montpellier in France, where a man aged 53 survived severe cold despite having no discernible heartbeat at all. He was discovered in a state of hypothermia; the core body temperature was 22 degrees. He was kept alive until, on rewarming, his body temperature had reached the normal 37 degrees; he was then resuscitated. Apart from the fact that the cardiac massage required to restart his heart resulted in cracked ribs the man appeared otherwise unharmed. Cold then had protected his heart and his brain although, of course, this was whole body cooling rather than just cooling the heart. As the residing doctor observed this was an 'extraordinary medical and human adventure'. He was certainly correct.

There is another meaning of 'cold'. A cold heart means chilled, unemotional, distant, unfriendly. Thus 'cold shoulder' means indifference, a rebuff, a snub. Not to be confused with 'cold feet'! 'The love of many will grow cold'[3] was Jesus' prediction of what would happen to some of his followers in the end days, meaning that their love and zeal would wane[4] whereas 'those who endure to the end will be saved'.[5]

Let us turn now from cold to heat. There is an ancient belief that the heart is an agent of heating. This is true, as measurements of the temperature of the blood entering and leaving the heart demonstrate. 'Blood is warm, perfect and full of spirit' so said William Harvey the discoverer of the circulation of the blood. 'Heart-warming' is usually linked with encouragement and compassion but there are at least two places in Scripture where the phrase 'my heart became hot' and 'there was in my heart as it were a burning fire' refers to either the build-up of frustration (Psalm 39) or an intensity

---

3   Matthew 24:12.

4   Revelation 2:4.

5   Matthew 24:13.

of feeling, an inner compulsion, a driving call from God that cannot be denied.[6]

Psalm 39 'the finest elegy in the Psalter', is one of the penitential psalms expressing repentance, sorrow for sin. 'My heart was hot within me, while I was musing the fire burned' (v. 3) or, as Pamela Greenberg translates, 'Then I grew restless and irritable, my heart grew hot within'. An initial attempt at suppressing sin led to feelings of repression, 'dumb with silence, I held my peace, my sorrow was stirred', a build-up of frustration. The psalmist (David) was getting worked up about things over which he had little control. That is, until the pressure breaks out in words and relief, came with prayer, 'Lord, make me to know my days and the measure of my days, what it is, that I may know how frail I am' (v. 4). 'Hot' because up to that point he could not speak.

The Jeremiah passage comes following the experience of the prophet not as a consequence of the awareness of sin (as with David) but, following his conflict with Pashur the official, perhaps also a priest. With this conflict came persecution, being beaten, mocked, his message unpopular. He himself became a laughingstock, a laughingstock who was then put in the physical stocks.[7] His situation, compelled to undertake a work against his will, led to a cry of utter dereliction against God ('Thou hast deceived me' v. 7). Walking a spiritual tight rope and facing the question 'suppose I am wrong' (always a mark of spiritual maturity) led to his decision not to make mention of God nor speak any more in his name (v. 9). Until that is God's word became to him 'in my heart as a burning fire shut up in my bones'. Not to go on like this was impossible. No longer speak any more the word of the Lord? Quite out of the question. He had moved from intense self-doubt and inner turmoil and profoundly discouraging service - obsessed with (apparent) failure and deciding to 'call it a day' – to this inner compulsion: 'In my heart as it were a burning fire', from being 'weary of holding it in' to 'I cannot withhold'. This is the word I am called to pronounce. Here then the phrase 'a burning fire' means intense, ardent, strongly emotional.

The other scriptural reference to the heart as a 'burning fire' (hot indeed) comes in Luke's gospel and is 'among the most beautiful of the treasures he alone has preserved for us'. This is the well-known account of the meeting of the risen Lord with the two disciples, I think man and wife, on the homeward

---

6   Jeremiah 20:9.

7   Jeremiah 20:1-9.

road to the village of Emmaus.[8] One can imagine the state of their hearts following the cataclysmic events of the first Good Friday; all their hopes dashed by the death by crucifixion of Jesus. Now physically dead, indeed the body already decomposing. Putrefaction, 'the most telling symbol of man's desperation'. Lazarus, in the tomb just one day longer, was already 'stinking'.[9] On the way they meet a stranger, to them a 'visitor'. 'Jesus himself drew near and went with them' (v. 15).

A telling phrase this, Jesus prepared to be where they were, the two then sharing their distraught with him, opening their hearts. And, as Jesus opened to them the Old Testament Scriptures we read 'did not our hearts burn within us while he talked with us'. We note that they did not say 'it dawned on them' or even 'they saw the light'. No, this was for them a quite new experience. It was radical. They had not experienced anything like this before. There followed a new confidence, a new joy, a new energy for that walk back to Jerusalem, retracing their steps to tell others, a new life born in them. In their hearts the spiritual life had begun. They had become different people as a result of this meeting. They suddenly realised who this 'stranger' was; he was 'known to them in the breaking of the bread'. A living meeting with the risen Christ. Many, many, years later John Wesley had a similar experience of the living Christ 'I felt my heart strangely warmed. I did feel I did trust in Christ, in Christ alone for salvation'. And, this is too the experience of many since.

Incidentally, the Greek word used here for 'burning' (v. 32) means 'to set fire to', to 'kindle'. It is the word also used for spiritual light,[10] opening dark hearts to the light of the good news.

---

8 Luke 24:13-35.

9 John 11:17, 39.

10 Luke 12:35; John 5:35.

I is for INSIDE THE HEART

'You formed my inward parts.'[1]

A letter to the medical journal Lancet in 2006 was about 'a heart within the heart, exploring the human heart'. The inside story. Or, as in Shakespeare's *Hamlet* 'my heart's core, ay, in my heart of heart'. But in physical terms what does the inside of the human heart really look like?

Many years ago, over fifty in fact, one of my PhD students was interested in the responses of coronary vessels to naturally occurring substances, normally found in and released by the heart, such as the neurotransmitters adrenaline, noradrenaline and acetylcholine. The preparation used was simple and a favourite of budding pharmacologists interested in the cardiovascular system; isolated blood vessels, in this case isolated coronary arteries. In order to study these someone from the department in which I worked went early to the local abattoir to collect pig hearts that would otherwise have been discarded. The hearts that is, not the pigs. First however a digression!

There is a long history of eating animal hearts. Hearts certainly not discarded! There is grim narrative, in that delightful book called *Carrying the Heart* by the American pathologist Frank Gonzalez-Crussi, about the legend, found in the lyrical poem *'lai d'Ignaure'* by the 12ᵗʰ C (or early 13ᵗʰ C) composer Renaut de Beaujeu, about the eating of (human) hearts. There are many other such stories on this subject, equally horrific, from the middle ages to the 20ᵗʰ century. I was, during a visit to the USA, given a cookbook to take home to my wife. This was *James Beard's American Cookbook*. In it was an interesting recipe (albeit still untried by my wife) of stuffed beef heart in which, before roasting, the heart was sewed together, using a large needle and heavy cords, in order to resemble its original shape. Can one I wonder purchase in my local butcher's shop the necessary main ingredient? Makers of that favourite (?) Scottish dish haggis keep secret the ingredients and composition of 'sheep and calf's offal', a word the *Oxford Dictionary*

---

1 Psalm 139:13.

describes as 'the less valuable edible parts of a carcass'. But is heart muscle involved?

To return to the pig hearts brought to the laboratory from the local abattoir. Although the main coronary arteries, as in the human heart, lie on the surface and therefore easy to dissect free from the underlying cardiac muscle, it was interesting to explore by dissection the inside of these discarded hearts. What is inside? However, before we come to that here is yet another digression especially for young budding research scientists, should there be any reading this book! It emphasises the importance in scientific research of expecting (or in this case of not expecting) the unexpected.

My Ghanaian PhD student used a technique beloved of physiologists and especially pharmacologists from time immemorable. The removed arteries are cut into segments or strips and placed in a small glass (organ) bath surrounded by a nutrient solution and bubbled with oxygen. The structure of these vessels is fascinating, consisting of an outer layer of (smooth) muscle and a non-muscular inner layer called the endothelium. The activity of the muscle layer is then recorded mechanically or, as at present, electronically. When noradrenaline is added to the fluid in the organ bath the preparation, perhaps surprisingly to some, relaxes through 'receptors' in the muscle membrane (or so we thought) called beta-adrenoceptors. However, if the arteries are left in the refrigerator overnight (or for a couple of days) noradrenaline causes, not a relaxation of the muscle but a contraction, an effect mediated through alpha-adrenoceptors.

Why this change in response? We never investigated this phenomenon. If we had we might have discovered something which later proved to be of enormous physiological significance. Indeed, years later, using a similar technique, Bob Furchgott won a Nobel Prize for the discovery that the inner lining of blood vessels (the endothelium) contains vasodilator substances, principally nitric oxide, which are essential in mediating vascular responses. He did this by recording vessel responses resulting from the mechanical removal of the endothelium. Had he done this, we wondered, by storing the coronary vessels in a cool environment and destroying or damaging the endothelium and so modifying the responses in the way we had observed years earlier? Always not only expect the unexpected in science, as in life, but then explore why this happened.

Let us return to what the inside of a heart looks like. There are at least two obvious structures; the cardiac muscle itself (very little, if any, fat) much thicker on the left than on the right and with no communication between the two, and the heart valves. These are situated between the atria and the ventricles and at the junctions of the major vessels. The structure of these valves is fascinating; they consist of leaflet like tissue the free ends of which are attached to the inner muscle wall through finger-like protruding papillary muscles. The leaflets function a little like yacht sails, ballooning when the pressure inside the ventricles increases, such that the free ends touch, this closes the aperture; when the pressure inside the heart decreases the leaflets collapse allowing blood to flow into the ventricles. This is a little like yacht sails 'collapsing' when there is no wind. The function of these beautiful structures, which open and close about forty million times a year, is to allow flow in only one direction, preventing back-flow. If they do not close properly then the valves cannot prevent regurgitation and are said to be incompetent or 'leaky'. They need to be replaced surgically.

This is nowadays a fairly common procedure, either with some form of mechanical valve or tissue valves called homografts. Conversely, the valves may 'stick' so that blood cannot easily flow through them, a condition called valve stenosis. Both valve incompetence and stenosis can put extra strain on the heart. One of the major causes of valve disease is wear and tear, a consequence of high blood pressure, or the deposition of calcium from the blood causing them to harden and to stiffen. These are often a consequence of ageing.

The other truly amazing property of the heart 'seen from the inside' is that, although the thickness of the muscle wall is so different on the left side to that on the right (the left ventricular wall mass is about three times that of the right) the output of the two ventricles is remarkably precise; the two ventricle are 'in step' with one another, there is no competition between then, the output from each side of the heart is precisely the same. It is possible to calculate what would happen if this were not so. Indeed, the consequence of a slight difference in output between the two sides of the heart would be disastrous even if this were to be small, say 0.2ml. Blood would accumulate either in the pulmonary circulation (most likely since this is a low-pressure system) or in the rest of the body. When one considers that the output varies markedly, it could be up to 25 litres a minute in severe exercise, this precision is amazing. It leaves this particular physiologist with a deep sense of wonder! Those mathematically inclined might like to calculate how much blood would accumulate in the pulmonary circulation, and hence in the lungs, over a 24 hour period if there were to be a difference in output of just 0.2 ml, the left pump exceeding the right by this amount. How long, do you think, would it take for the heart to fail because of a 'build up' of blood behind the deficient right ventricle and ultimately into the pulmonary venous circulation?

We have thought above just a little about heart structure, the 'heart within the heart'. How could this relate to the spiritual heart, the heart the Lord 'looks upon'?[2] Well, 'in' (within) is an 'in' word. The word means basically 'contained by' or 'surrounded by'. We live in an atmosphere of air containing the oxygen we need for survival; we are surrounded by it, we are 'within' it, we are 'inside'.

Scripture is full of this word 'in'. For example, Jesus in John's gospel (chapter 15) talks to his disciples about 'abiding in', making our home 'in him', of 'remaining in' him and in his love. Here the illustration is of the branch abiding in the vine plant. The word 'in' comes no fewer than thirteen times in verses 4 to 11. Clearly then Jesus is here making an important point. Further, this is no short time for 'abiding in' since we are to remain, stay in Christ and in his love; we are all to be 'remainers'! But then we are also told that Christ is 'in' us, his word and his love are to remain, to stay, 'in us'. This word 'in', 'inside', thus describes an intimate relationship between the Lord Jesus Christ and us as individuals; here Jesus was speaking to his disciples as individuals. The word 'in' thus describes our so close relationship with Jesus, and not only with him with but God the Father as well. The result is we are called friends of Jesus (v. 14), prayer is answered (v. 7) and there is abundant joy (v. 11). There are, of course, conditions to our remaining; for example, obedience (v. 10) and love (v. 12). This was Jesus' prayer for the church.[3] 'In' then becomes a common and important word in the New Testament. There are countless examples not only in John's gospel[4] but elsewhere.[5] Could anything in the spiritual life be more fundamental than being 'in'?

---

2   1 Samuel 16:7.

3   John 17:21, 23.

4   John 6:56; 10:38; 14:10, 11, 20, 21; 17:23, 26.

5   Romans 8:10.

But it is puzzling, this use of the word 'in', 'inside', to describe this personal relationship between us and Jesus. This is because Jesus is not only in us but we are, at the same time, also in him. Is there a simple example that might help us to grasp this great truth? Perhaps the example of the air we breathe might help. Not however, the polluted air of our cities and streets but the purer air on the summit of a Scottish mountain perhaps. Wherever we live, we breathe in air containing the essential component for our physical life on earth because that air, we might say wonderfully, contains oxygen the very 'stuff of life'.

I remember once on the Isle of Arran seeing a notice in a local garage – 'air available here'. Wonderful that it is available! Everywhere. Then we also have been given the essential apparatus, the lungs, to make use of this 'air' and the oxygen contained in it. So, we are in, surrounded by, the air and that same air is also in us. In the same way by his Spirit, Christ (by invitation) invades the heart; it is his Spirit that is 'in the inner man'.[6]

---

6 Ephesians 3:16.

J is for THE JOYFUL, HAPPY HEART

'Happy is that people whose God is the LORD'.[1]
'Rejoice in the Lord always'.[2]
'The joy of the Lord is your strength'.[3]
'Your words became to me a joy and the delight of my heart.'[4]

We here look at two heart-related words that deal with well-being: 'happy' (happiness) which comes rather infrequently in Scripture, and 'joy' (joyous) which comes often. Certainly, as we shall see, both profoundly affect the physical heart. First then, happy – the 'happy heart'.

I was wondering how we know whether our hearts are happy or not? My conclusion is that most of the time our physical hearts are very happy. Why? Because our beating hearts are fulfilling the task for which they were intended – pumping. If unhappy I do not believe it would still be functioning well – as mine is as I write. Our hearts are always giving out, serving the needs of the body, doing what they were meant to do. So, this generous giving out makes our hearts very happy! All that blood given away every time they beat. Generosity makes it, and us, very happy. As the Scottish singer, entertainer (and hero) Sir Harry Lauder had it, 'Aye, I'm tellin ye happiness is one of the few things in this world that doubles every time you share it with someone else'. And, as Jesus said, 'it is more blessed (happy) to give than to receive'.[5] Our hearts do both, giving and receiving at the same time – and they do this very well! Job well done. Indeed, superbly done. Happy hearts.

So, what is happiness? Is it, for example the same as 'well-being'? There have been many attempts to define and describe it. There is, for example, the

---

1   Psalm 144:15.
2   Philippians 4:4.
3   Nehemiah 8:10.
4   Jeremiah 15:16.
5   Acts 20:35.

attempt by the Office of National Statistics in Britain to measure 'national well-being'; a minister for well-being perhaps? A cabinet appointment? Or by the Organization of Economic Cooperation and Development (OECD) with its 'better life index', focussing on 'life-satisfaction', work-life balance, health and education. This is close to Aristotle's view that 'happiness comes from living well and practising virtue'. All very positive. The 'good life'. Or again, and rather delightfully, the description of the economy of the small country of Bhutan in the Himalayan mountains in terms of 'gross national happiness'.

The psychologist Cliff Arnall, a 'happiness coach' for a number of 'celebrities' and business leaders and a former university lecturer, fed into his computer a 'happiness' formula which took into account factors including the weather, social interaction, holiday anticipation, being outdoors and childhood summer memories. He 'discovered' that, at least for Scotland, the 'happiness day of the year' is the third Friday in June! This was far back in 2014 when he added to his formula factors such as the belief that Andy Murray would again win Wimbledon! Indeed, sport makes some happy – especially when they, or their team, wins. The, perhaps tongue in cheek, suggestion by one GP that golf should be on his prescription pad! Putting rather than pills? Three holes twice a day? Then, there is the perceptive comment about the relationship between happiness and health; an optimistic attitude on life with that infectious smile, a happiness that does not depend on outward circumstances but is the 'fruit' of the inner heart. As for the world capital place for 'well-being', Melbourne in Australia came out as the best place in the world to live in. Not surprising. With Orkney not too far behind.

In English there are several words to express this well-being – happiness, joy (rejoicing, enjoyment), a deep feeling of gladness, contentment, pleasure, cheerful, all with a slightly different connotation. Tom Wright translates the first word of the beatitudes in Matthew 5, usually translated as 'happy' or 'blessed' as 'wonderful news'! It is.

In Scripture, there are two words that seem interchangeable and which are translated as either happy or blessed. In NT Greek the word *makarios* is variously translated as 'happy', fortunate[6] but in these places 'blessed' would have done just as well. Elsewhere[7] the same word is translated as 'happy' in the AV but as 'blessed' in the RV and ESV. Is there a difference? There is! In

---

6   Acts 26:2 and Romans 14:22.

7   John 13:17; 1 Peter 3:14 and 4:14.

the well-known passage on the 'beatitudes'[8] about the values of the kingdom of God, the word is 'blessed' in most versions (AV, ESV, NIV) but 'happy' in the J.B. Phillips version. Phillips is better! As Dick France has pointed out 'blessed' is a misleading translation, since blessed is a quite different Greek word (*eulogitos*). Happy is better 'so long as it is used as a condition of life'– fortunate, 'well off', well-being; it is a spiritual quality rather than a mental state. We are 'happy' if we are humble-minded (poor in spirit), merciful, we make peace, are hungry and thirsty for goodness, righteous (righteousness, our life orientation towards God) but also when we are persecuted on account of Jesus. In such conditions we are to 'rejoice and be glad' – happy if we stand for God. 'Blessed are those who know what sorrow means'[9] who are ill-treated and persecuted 'for the cause of goodness'. That is, if we fulfil the purpose for which God made us – fellowship with him and the discovery of his personal will for us whatever that may mean.

Who then are the happy ones? We are certainly happy when we are blessed by God. It means, says Eugene Peterson, 'unanticipated good fortune, a sense of surprise, an unexpected gift'. How does this come about? A good starting place is Psalm 1, that prologue to the whole book of psalms. 'Blessed (happy) is he whose delight is in the law of the Lord'[10] that is, the teaching which shows God's way to happiness. When we delight in God's word, when we think around it, ponder, meditate, we then chew, 'masticate' God's word. This is because delight suggests something unhurried. It is a leisurely and time-consuming art. It means taking a lingering view. It reflects, savours, appreciates and enjoys. Before rushing into the rest of the day there is all the difference in the world between that quick read of a verse or two of Scripture (with the sometimes rather superficial written comment upon it) and the time spent 'thinking around' God's word and then turning it over in our heart and mind throughout the day.

It is through intimacy with the Lord that we are 'blessed'. Listening to his voice through his word. So, the word 'blessed' in the Old Testament means God's favour, it expresses his concern for us. We are dependent upon him for our existence and function, we are content, even though our outward individual or social circumstances may be such that the word 'happiness' could hardly describe them.

---

8 Matthew 5:2-12.

9 Matthew 5:4.

10 Psalm 1:1, 2.

In summary then, for Christians perhaps to be happy means fulfilling, just like our mechanical hearts, the purpose for which we were created. Indeed, the first occurrence in Scripture, which is also God's first word to man, implies this – 'God blessed them and said be fruitful and multiply'.[11] Be happy.

We should mention that 'to bless' has another meaning. It means to praise, although this is mostly a quite different word (in Hebrew, *halal*). We 'bless' the Lord,[12] and in many modern songs – 'Bless the Lord O my soul, worship his holy name', 'Blessed be the name of the Lord' – and so many others. The two meanings come together in Psalm 134, one of the psalms of pilgrimage. It begins with the word 'bless' meaning 'praise' (v. 1, 2); the servants of the Lord are to 'come' and 'bless (praise) the Lord' and then, at the end of the psalm (v. 3) there is the request, a prayer, for the Lord, the creator God, to bless us, for God to delight in us (amazing thought) just as we are to delight in God. Every heart is happy!

However, happiness, the 'happy heart' is surely the weakest of those words describing pleasure, well-being. The meaning of joy, both in normal speech and in Scripture is rather different. We are 'tickled pink' by happiness but we are not 'over the moon' or 'up in the air'. Happiness perhaps is quieter, rather sedate, in control, it does not ordinarily imply the excitement and strong feeling of joy. Joy then is more vivid; the *Oxford Dictionary* uses explanatory words like ecstasy, elated, euphoric – the three e's of joy.

If the physical heart is happy because of what it is doing, fulfilling its purpose, what can we say of the 'joyful heart', those times when our hearts are leaping for joy? Albeit fortunately not out of the chest! There are certainly times when our hearts beat a little faster. Here I am not talking about exercise but those times when we have a vivid emotion of pleasure: times when our hearts, because they are a part of us, are indeed elated, ecstatic. Euphoric even. We can all think of such times, when we are 'over the moon', that sensation of surprise (by joy) when we fall in love, when our first, and subsequent, children or grandchildren are born, when we receive an unexpected visit from a child living on the other side of the world. Then, we are on 'cloud nine', 'head over heels', 'up in the air', 'on top of the world'. All these phrases suggest adventure, physical movement to faraway places – to the top of the world, clouds, air. In the mind at least. True too of the

---

11 Genesis 1:22, 28.

12 for example, Psalm 103:1, 2, 21, 22.

spiritual life, when joy comes and we can hardly 'hold it in'. C.S. Lewis was not surprised by happiness, when he moved from unbelief to that place where he found the reality of Christ, but he was surprised by joy, the serious business of heaven! Hearts leaping for joy! William Tyndale described the Christian faith as 'good, merry, glad, joyful tidings' that 'maketh a mannes hert glad and makes hym sing and dance'. This is more than happiness. You may not shout when you are happy, but joyful occasions make you want to shout out loud. True too in our spiritual lives, the joy of corporate worship singing the great songs of salvation. On top of the world when you feel like dancing. And our physical hearts take an active role in this deep sense of joy since they are an essential part of us.

Also, this word means rejoicing in hope,[13] in giving willingly[14] indeed, in all circumstances[15] but especially it means rejoicing in the Lord himself[16] and taking refuge in him.[17] This is the noisy joy of praise![18] This joy comes with God's blessing because it is the joy of Christ himself.[19] It is the joy of the Father who had found his lost son.[20] It results in corporate 'joy in heaven over one sinner that repents' and in which all the 'sons of God' join.[21] God's creation commenced with joy. We can imagine God's smile when he pronounced all things 'good'[22] whilst at the end of time there is still an even more abundant joy,[23] assembled, exuberant, hilarious joy when 'all creation joins in joy'. And, joy everywhere in between, from the beginning to the end of time!

So, on what does joy depend? It certainly depends on being loved and trusted. Of course, human love is an immense help, often stimulating as well as comforting. Yet human love so often fails to chase away the gloom when we meet in life with sickness, separation, anxiety or death. But where

13 Romans 12:12.
14 1 Chronicles 29:9.
15 1 Thessalonians 5:16.
16 Psalm 32:11, 33:1, 64:10, 97:12, Luke 1:47.
17 Psalm 2:12.
18 Psalms 66:1, 95:1, 98:4, 100:1.
19 John 15:11, 17:13.
20 Luke 15:23, 24.
21 Job 38:7.
22 Genesis 1:12, 18, 21, 25, 31.
23 Revelation 4:1-11.

human love can fail Divine love succeeds. It is big enough to take in the whole world yet individual enough to weep, as at the grave of Lazarus. Sometimes this sense of love for us is such that we find it difficult to restrain the overflowing, tumultuous sense of joy. As Francis Xavier wrote 'I prayed to God to restrain the overwhelming fullness of joy which constantly filled my soul'. This is joy that comes from the sense of wonder and the excitement that follows the realisation the we are loved by Almighty God, that we are chosen by him, that Jesus died and rose again as a practical demonstration of such love, that he wants to fulfil all his glorious purposes for us. Joy then results from the realisation that we are so deeply loved by our Heavenly Father.

Such joy is not affected by outward circumstances. Paul rejoiced in his 'afflictions',[24] in what was happening in the churches, despite opposition. He was joyful because of their growth in likeness to Christ, their love for one another (and for him) and their 'joy in the Lord'. But the most striking example of joy in affliction was the joy of Jesus himself. 'My joy will be in you. Your joy will be full'[25] words said in the last few days before his death. Joy spoken in the context of love, the Father's love for him and Jesus' love for his friends. There had been the washing of the disciple's feet, the Passover meal, the betrayal and the looking forward to Gethsemane, the vicious hatred, the arrest, the trials, the gross injustice and the horrific death. Yet, in such circumstances Jesus speaks about 'joy', his joy, a shared inexpressible joy 'a joy unspeakable and full of glory'.[26]

We cannot leave the subject of happiness and joy without saying something about laughter. Laughter really does affect the heart, increasing heart rate, blood pressure and the release of catecholamines. There is an enhanced return of blood to the heart leading presumably, to an increase in cardiac output. The increase in ventilation leads to enhanced clearing of mucus which aids, for example, patients with chronic pulmonary conditions. However, the most interesting cardiovascular effect is on the endothelium, that inner lining of the blood vessels. Dr Michael Millar made people laugh whilst measuring forearm arterial blood flow; this increased by over 20%. It involved the endothelium releasing vasoactive substances (nitric oxide perhaps?) to enhance flow. In contrast, emotional stress reduces arterial

24 2 Corinthians 7:4.
25 John 15:11.
26 1 Peter 1:8.

blood flow by about the same extent. 'The benefit of laughter to blood vessel health is equal to that of aerobic activity'. This raises interesting questions. Replace jogging with jokes? A daily dose of hilarity lasting fifteen minutes? Laughter really is good medicine. One can imagine the 'joy unspeakable' of the psalmist[27] 'when the Lord restored the fortunes of Zion our mouths were filled with laughter and out tongues with shouts of joy'. Laughing and shouting at the same time? Those endothelial cells must have been hyperactive!

Laughing and humour. Perhaps Jesus told some of his parables with a twinkle in his eye; camels getting though the eye of a needle, the fabricated excuses made for not following him such as buying pieces of land without first seeing it, spending money on oxen without examining them first. 'I have married a wife' seems more plausible. Perhaps! It seems that Jesus was well aware that humour penetrates deeper and achieves more than open rebuke. Through the 'mirthquake', the 'still small voice'. The Bible tells us that there will be no more tears in heaven but says nothing about laughter. Yet how could we live without it? Joy! What a saving grace it is!

There is one other biblical incident linking laughter with real joy. It concerns the story about Sarah and Abraham's first-born son Isaac – which name itself is perhaps an abbreviation of Isaac-El, meaning 'God laughs'. After the birth Sarah says[28] 'all that hear (this miraculous news) will laugh with (or over) me', 'God has made laughter for me'. So, God makes laughter. And this laughter-filled joy was infectious, 'all joined in' the divine pleasure. This is universal laughter at unadulterated joy, 'glad tidings of great joy'. Previously when Sarah laughed[29] it was from unbelief, incredulity; now it was the laughter of joy, the joy of fulfilment (at long last), of astonishment, incredulity, surprise and satisfaction. Great news of great joy!

---

27 Psalm 126:2.

28 Genesis 21:6, 7.

29 Genesis 18:13.

Above all else, guard your **heart**, for it is the wellspring of life ......Proverbs 4:23

K is for the KEPT, GUARDED HEART

'Above all else, guard your heart, for it is the wellspring of life.'[1]

The word 'keep' means to preserve from harm, to guard thoroughly with great carefulness, to retain in one's possession, to maintain in good condition. To keep safe, to watch over.

When applied to the human physical heart to keep or guard is concerned with what we can do to help maintain it in as sound a condition as possible, in good working order. So, this 'keeping' has to do with lifestyle and the changes we might have to make to help keep our heart in 'tip top' condition.

The spiritual implications of the words, 'keep', 'guard', which come frequently in Scripture, firstly have to do with what we ourselves have to do to maintain our hearts in good order. We have to guard our hearts;[2] positively this means to keep God's commands and covenant;[3] it is we then who are to keep watch over ourselves.[4] Negatively, there are things we are to

---

1   Proverbs 4:23.

2   Proverbs 22:5.

3   Genesis 17:9; Exodus 20:6.

4   Galatians 6:1.

'keep away' from,[5] to keep at arms length, to keep our lives free from,[6] things that could be detrimental to good heart function. However, as we shall see, the main emphasis is on God himself. He is the One who keeps, who guards 'covers' and shelters: He is our keeper, our custodian and guardian, it is God's peace that guards.[7] 'The Lord bless you and KEEP you'.[8]

A heathy lifestyle can do much to keep our physical heart from malfunction and to ensure that it continues to beat strongly, adapting to all life's circumstances, for as long as possible. We have thought a little about the positive effects of exercise; we now turn to another major influence for keeping our hearts functioning well and that is the consequences for the heart that arise from the food we eat, the protecting effects, or overwise, of diet.

'Man shall not live by bread alone'[9] not 'man shall not live by bread'. The key word in that saying of Jesus is 'alone'. We do need more than bread but we also do need bread – food. But what kind of food? How much of it and how does what we eat affect the heart? Are there foods that are detrimental to heart function and are there foods that are 'good for the heart'? And, food should be both 'fun and healthy' says a British Heart Foundation booklet.

Nearly forty years ago the American Heart Association published their *Heartbook*, a guide to the prevention and treatment of cardiovascular disease. Of course, it contained a chapter on diet and nutrition. Even earlier, in 1977, the American cardiologist Paul Kezdi published his book, long out of print, called *You and Your Heart* – how to take care of your heart for a long and healthy life. In his Preface to the book Professor Peter Sleight, then at the Radcliffe Infirmary in Oxford, commented on the controversy about diet and the heart and wrote that 'there is no doubt that that our (UK) eating habits have changed profoundly in the last 25 years; we take much more of our food as fat compared with carbohydrate than formerly'.

So what, forty years after these words were written, has changed? Is it possible to eat and drink 'heart-saving' foods and beverages in order to keep our hearts guarded and safe? For, in a different context, as the psalmist wrote 'the heart, the life spring of all desires, must be guarded'. This may

5   Psalm 19:13.
6   Hebrews 13:5.
7   Philippians 4:7.
8   Numbers 6:24.
9   Matthew 4:4; Luke 4:4.

involve changing our eating (and drinking) habits. We may come to like foods we have not tasted before! There should be a sense of adventure, as well as pleasure, in what we eat.

Much advice has been given about 'diet and the heart'. It is not the intention here to add to this but simply to summarise what we know about food and 'guarding' the heart, 'keeping' it safe.

First, we need enough food to satisfy the regular daily energy needs of the body and to provide for the maintenance, growth, repair and renewal of each body cell. Energy is measured in units called calories; one calorie is defined as 'the amount of energy required to raise the temperature of one litre (about one quart in "old money") of water by one degree Celsius'! The most important sources of energy, and the body's main building blocks, are fats, carbohydrates and proteins. These are called 'macronutrients'. 'Micronutrients', as their name suggests, are nutrients needed in smaller amounts like vitamins and minerals.

Calorie intake should balance energy expenditure. If you are above your 'ideal weight' the need is to reduce your calorie intake. To give some idea of how much energy is expended let us take some everyday examples. If, like me now, you spend a lot of time at a desk you might expect to expend daily about 2,000 calories; of this, two to three hours reading or watching the TV would account for about 350 calories, light work around the house (for me, washing up) would burn another 250 calories. Sleeping for seven hours would consume about another 500 calories. Why does sleep consume as many calories as that? Because during sleep our brains are busy, sorting information, repairing damaged neurones whilst our muscles still move a little and hopefully, our hearts are still beating. Total daily energy expenditure for a largely sedentary person would thus be about 2,000 to 2,500 calories. Note that these numbers should really be as kilocalories but in discussions about nutrition they are generally referred to simply as calories. Energy expenditure is considerably lower in ageing; elderly people do not need to eat as they did when young. Of course, when you are active, doing exercise or manual work, your energy expenditure would be very much more than this and you must eat accordingly.

So, on the intake side of the equation we need enough food to meet the metabolic needs of the body. But, what kind of food? First then, for a healthy heart, and indeed for a healthy body, since the food we eat affects our overall health, we need a healthy diet. We are what we eat. So, what constitutes a healthy diet? As Thomas Love Peacock once wrote about drinking: 'There are two reasons for drinking; one is when you are thirsty to cure thirst; the other is when you are not thirsty, to prevent it'. Prevention is better than cure! So, what then is a healthy diet? In a report many years ago by the British Cardiac Society (now the British Cardiovascular Society) the healthy diet was defined as a balanced diet. 'Food should be fun . . . and healthy'. This means it should contain all the important ingredients. These are proteins, which are 'body cell builders', replacing cells that are deteriorating, carbohydrates (energy sources which the body quickly uses) and fats (which are an important energy source for the heart when broken down to fatty acids). These three are the macromolecules. The acceptable macronutrient distribution is protein (10-25%), carbohydrates (45-65%) and fats (20-35%). In addition, we also require adequate amounts of the micronutrients, minerals, vitamins and the various trace metals such as zinc, selenium, iron and chromium. By the way all of these are contained in a normal, 'healthy diet'; no need to 'supplement' these further. These 'supplements' lighten your pocket without helping your heart.

This is not a book of nutrition; the British Heart Foundation (bhf.org. uk) has a good (and free) guide to healthy eating with lots of nutritious recipes. In brief, a diet rich in fruit, vegetables, whole grain bread, high-fibre cereals and fish but low in saturated fats, reduces the risk of developing heart disease. Some advocate increasing unsaturated fat (found for example in sunflower and oily fish oils and also in olive oil) as part of any dietary regime for the population at large. This is in part because they can lower cholesterol levels. It is especially important to choose the quality and quantity of the fats we eat because of its profound impact on cardiovascular health and disease. Ideally, fats make up about 30% of our energy input so cutting out fat altogether makes little sense. But what kind of fat? Both fats and oils are high in calories but saturated and so called 'trans' fats are to be avoided since they elevate cholesterol levels, especially the harmful LDL cholesterol which increases the risk of fatty deposits in the blood vessels. This is especially damaging in the coronary arteries in the heart. Such saturated and 'trans' fats are found in butter, hard cheese, dripping, cream, pastries, deep fried foods and fatty meat.

The question for us is this. What foods are detrimental to the proper functioning of the heart and which foodstuffs have a positive effect on it, guarding and keeping it from harm? One way of approaching this question is to compare the incidence of heart disease in different communities and see if there is any relationship with what those communities eat and drink. When we look at mortality rates among different populations from, for example, coronary artery disease then certain clear and incontrovertible conclusions may be drawn. The best of these studies is historical because the later popularity of present day western (predominantly American) dietary habits tends to confuse the picture, especially in Europe and Asia. The question then is, are there countries where the mortality from cardiovascular disease is low (or has been low in the past before the incursion of American fast food style diets) in comparison with other countries? The answer to that question, first posed many years ago, is yes. Japan, France and Italy had, and indeed still have, a lower incidence of cardiovascular disease, especially coronary artery disease, than in the UK or the USA. This is true both for men and women. The difference in incidence is three to four-fold for coronary heart disease and rather less for cardiovascular disease in general. Life expectancy is again higher in Japan and in certain areas of France and Italy than in the UK and the USA.

The question is why this difference? Is diet mainly, even partially, responsible? Are there protective factors involved? Do some communities eat foods that are less damaging to the heart? The French diet, for example, is unusual because although it includes dairy products (cheese, butter, milk) which contain 'bad cholesterol' (and a great deal of sugar) the annual death rate from coronary events, is much less (indeed, five times less for women) in cities such as Strasburg, Lille, Toulouse than in Glasgow, despite other risk factors (elevated systolic arterial blood pressure, smoking, cholesterol levels) being similar. A paradox. A French paradox. A 'most ingenious paradox' to quote W.S. Gilbert. Ingenious indeed! But this should really be called the Mediterranean paradox. Angela Merkel, the German President called these countries the 'Club med' and this is where people tend to live longer. The conclusion from such studies might be that there is something protective in this diet, guarding the heart, 'keeping' it safe. This so-called 'Mediterranean diet' is largely based on vegetables, fruit, nuts, fish and unsaturated ('good') fats like olive oil. And, perhaps a good French red wine?

But, is there something else which is important for the guarding, the keeping of the heart, something additional to the 'Club med' diet? I think there is, and that is lifestyle; 'il fait bon vivre'. It is more than about what we eat. It is about how we eat. Eating more slowly superb food served in smallish portions (maybe even ask for a child's portion!), families eating together and good conversations.

When I first visited the United States, as a consultant for various pharmaceutical companies, I was struck initially by two things. Hospitality, the great welcome into the homes I stayed in; and the absence of breakfast. We simply jumped in the car, drove a few miles and dropped off at the nearest eating place. We ate out because we were already out as one friend explained. Get on with the day. Time spent eating was important but took away from the business of the day. So, fast food. Then, after work, the rush home for frozen (rewarmed) food, often pizza. Time spent eating seemed to be wasted time. Not much talk.

Then I also spent much time, during a sabbatical and especially after I retired at the fixed age, living in Hungary. I do not remember in all those years times when we were not frequently invited guests for lunch or dinner. All the family present, from the youngest to the oldest; it all took time even though much of the food had been slow cooked from an early hour. Giving thanks before the meal, then several hours sitting at the dining table with much talk, often on spiritual matters, sharing together from God's word. Indeed, the only person absent for much of the time was the hostess, the lady of the house. She was in the kitchen, taking care of things, making sure everyone had what they needed. And she kept bringing in more! It took time, much time, and a great deal of care and effort to produce those meals. And, before it even started there was the time spent in the market selecting the 'best', essential ingredients. Of course, this is true in other European countries, France especially. Indeed, it is true elsewhere in the world; I think of the time taken to prepare a meal in Africa starting in the very early morning. How we eat then is as important as what we eat. Time, as one friend put it, is the 'secret ingredient'. Is this I wonder an important part of the 'heart guarding' Club med Mediterranean diet?

Before we leave the subject of diet and its effect on the heart yet another diversion, this time into the cardiac effects of chocolate, coffee and tea. Chocolate first; a sweetmeat made from the crushed seeds of the cacao tree. How about a daily dose? From its introduction into Europe in the 17th century, chocolate became a regular ingredient of prescriptions and pharmacopoeias for almost any bodily ill. Old pharmacopoeias have interesting recipes for chocolate, especially after the addition of cinnamon, pepper and vanilla in order to counteract the bitter taste. The book (and later a film) about the opening of a chocolaterie in a small French village comes to mind. As does the story of the Spanish Marquis de Mansera who lived entirely on chocolate and died at the age of 107! Was, I wonder, his heart protected by it? It seems that, like that one apple, one small square of dark chocolate a day 'keeps the doctor away'. In some reports there was a reduction in cardiac events of up to 40% in the risk of heart disease (and stroke) by regularly ingesting small amount of the 'dark stuff'.

But what about the calorie intake of eating chocolate? It is said that twenty M and S 'extremely chocolatery biscuits' would be your calorie ration for the day! This is because chocolate contains both fat and carbohydrate (making up to 500 calories per 100g) and this contributes to weight gain thus outweighing any benefits. But healthy? The 'food of the gods'? Chocolate was even at one time a source of currency; if Scotland becomes an independent country would this be a candidate for currency? But does chocolate help to keep the heart healthy? Well, it is like coffee a stimulant; dark chocolate contains both caffeine and theobromine; both may inhibit platelet aggregation and increase blood flow and, perhaps, lower blood pressure, like the chemically similar theophylline (found in tea). Chocolate also contain flavanols which promote antioxidant activity, decrease the activity of low-density (LD) lipoproteins, that carry cholesterol around the body, protect endothelial function and perhaps stimulate angiogenesis. Maybe as de Quelus noted in his *Natural History of Chocolate* published in 1719, it really is the 'milk of old men', it is to old men what milk is to infants. This old man would like to think so!

And coffee? The Western world is now a society of coffee drinkers. In the small town in which I live there are now seven coffee shops in a quite small shopping area, whereas when we first came to live in it over fifty years ago there was just one. Caffeine, which coffee contains, is the most commonly taken drug in the world. It is, of course, a cerebral stimulant, perhaps leading to the development of 'good ideas', it increases blood flow (especially renal blood flow) can, in high doses, increase heart rate (and in excess lead to atrial premature beats) and blood pressure (by as much as 10-25 mmHg) and increase gastric acid production contributing to the development of gastritis. Remembering the association between 'gut and heart', could caffeine-induced gastric ulceration contribute to coronary artery disease and myocardial infarction? Older studies, which however did not take into account either diet or exercise, might suggest so. Drinking six cups of coffee a day increases by twofold the risk of a myocardial infarction as compared with non-coffee drinkers.

I like the advice of one retired notary aged ninety-eight from a hillside village south of Naples. When asked about the success of his long life (still going) he emphasised his diet, typically Mediterranean, a small glass of red wine daily, a small cup of coffee, his (very light) physical activity, friendship, his reading (an hour or two each day), crosswords, not abandoning his 'intellectual' life and not straying too far from nature. However, best of all, his 'secrets' for a long and happy life were time, silence and love. Especially love. Good ways to guard the heart!

Now, spiritually how can we follow the injunction to guard our hearts? As with the physical heart forewarned is forearmed. The author of Proverbs emphasised the paramount importance of this. He writes 'above all else'[10] guard your heart. Why? Because he saw that the heart is the wellspring of life, that out of it comes the 'issues of life' and that it is the centre of affections and personality, our 'inner being'. Because it determines every aspect of our daily living, what we do, where we go, what we see, read, how we pray, what lingers in our minds. It is what shapes our lives, our lifestyles. So, we have to take care of it, to guard and keep it. We are to mind our spiritual steps, looking where we are going and determining how we are to get there. We are to 'make level paths for our feet',[11] what we say, what we hear and what we see. All very practical! This means that we are to be careful what we hold dear, what we treasure in our hearts. Perhaps these words from Proverbs were in the mind of Jesus when he talked about 'treasure within the heart'[12] and of 'the good treasure of the heart'[13] and perhaps also when he said 'out of the heart will flow rivers of living water' speaking of the indwelling Holy Spirit.[14] These treasures need to be guarded.

There are two relevant Hebrew words for keep and guard, *shamar* and *natsar*, which together come about five hundred times in the Old Testament. They are used, for example, of Adam in the garden, he was to tend and keep

---

10 Proverbs 4:23.

11 Proverbs 4:24-26.

12 Matthew 6:21.

13 Luke 6:45.

14 John 7:38, 39.

it[15] and of Harhas (or Hasrah) the keeper of the king's wardrobe.[16] It is also ironically, the word used by David chiding Abner for not 'keeping watch in order to keep the king safe'.[17] This ability to keep safe is used of God himself for example in Psalms 91 and especially in Psalm 121 where the words 'keep' (or 'keeper') comes six times in as many verses.

Psalm 91 is a song praising the security which is in God himself. It contains a whole battery of words to emphasis this – shelter, in the secret place, under the shadow of God Most High, covered with his pinions and under his wings. This a favourite figure in Hebrew literature[18] where the bird referred to is usually the mighty eagle. There is a camera in an osprey nest not far from where I live; when danger threatens, from a storm or from another bird, the young are sheltered under the huge (six feet span) wings of the parent bird.

Then, God is our refuge, fortress, our never sleeping, never slumbering guardian, 'keeping in all your ways',[19] we are held fast, gripped firmly, lifted up and set on high by him. We are 'at home' with God, abiding, dwelling, we have found lodging there suggesting a family's welcome, never refused, although we have no natural right to this as 'stateless refugees'. Wonderfully too, we are in his presence, 'with him'. Top security!

All this is very personal. You are 'my refuge' writes both David[20] and Jeremiah.[21] It is only God who keeps and guards ('other refuge have I none'), 'you' are my fortress and stronghold.[22] Then the psalmist widens this; God is the one who 'keeps you'[23] who 'preserves the way of his people'.[24] This keeping is all inclusive, kept from all evil, for all aspects of life, the whole of it, implicit in the words 'going out and coming in', leaving and returning. It is for all time, 'from this time forth and for evermore'.[25]

---

15 Genesis 2:15.
16 2 Kings 22:14.
17 1 Samuel 26:15.
18 Psalms 36:7; 61:4.
19 Psalm 121:4.
20 Psalm 62:7.
21 Jeremiah 17:17.
22 Psalms 31:3; 91:2.
23 Psalm 121:7, 8.
24 Proverbs 2:8.
25 Psalm 121:8.

However, there are problems in the interpretation of Psalm 91. Surely the 'dark' verses (5 to 7) cannot mean that no child of God has ever been 'struck down' by the terror of the night or been swept away by pestilence. It is not, as one supposedly eminent physician from St Petersburg once claimed, a preservative against cholera – or any other infectious disease (ebola, malaria, dengue, HIV). Arrow, plague (cancer, dementia) bullet and fire have reached Christians – and sadly, are still reaching them. It is not a guarantee of safety against the obstacles, difficulties and dangers that threaten life. Nor is it, as some have claimed, a guarantee of health or wealth. However, it certainly does not mean that God cannot miraculously intervene to preserve from physical peril; there are some quite wonderful examples of such interventions and also of dramatic healings. But not always.

When I was a relatively young Christian and working in Nigeria a family friend, Richard Earnshaw-Smith, Chaplain to the Bishop of Lagos, was killed in a VC10 air crash over that city. I wondered why. There was so much for him to do for the kingdom. Had he not prayed over this psalm many times and claimed these promises? John Stott has written 'only the children of God who are living in the will of God can expect the protection of God'. Certainly true and, I would believe, true also of Richard. How could God let this happen? So, what kind of protection is this?

I am writing these words a few days after the bombing of churches in Sri Lanka and the killings and rape of so many in parts of Nigeria and in several other West African countries. Christians do die from ebola, children of Christian parents are taken and recruited to become child soldiers after seeing their parents murdered before their eyes, whole villages are pillaged and burnt, child migrants are drowned at sea, cars and aeroplanes crash with believers on board. And what of the Jewish believers, for whom this psalm was originally written, on their way to the gas chambers? Clearly then God does not always intervene to preserve and keep his people from physical danger. There is no guarantee of safety as of right. What then can we draw from these 'security psalms', of the God who keeps and guards? Perhaps first we can say that God's security is eternal security. There is life beyond this present one. One kept in heaven. This life is not all there is. There is the promise of being in God's presence, even of being like Jesus! As the old Male Voice Praise hymn has it – 'one day we shall see him and one day we'll be like him, O what a day! All my sins washed away'. We can indeed be assured of God's presence at all times and in all places, even in the midst of terrible suffering.

We speak of the desolation that Jesus felt on the Cross of Calvary, where he died to secure the lives of those he loves. We think too of his loneliness – 'my God why have you forsaken me?' And yet was not the Father present at the Cross? When Jesus speaks of the disciples forsaking and leaving him he says, 'Yet I am not alone for the Father is with me'.[26] God is present with us in all the extremes of life – and death.

I think that sometimes God 'takes' someone dear to us because he loves that person so much that he wants him or her to be with him. So often this is sooner than those 'left behind' would like. Could it be that the work God had planned for them here on earth has ended? That their lives had now been brought into conformity with that pattern already set by God? And, as C.S. Lewis wrote 'Can you not see death as a friend and deliverer? What is there to be afraid of?' Peace. Let go. Underneath are the everlasting arms.

---

26 John 16:32.

L is for the LISTENING HEART

*'Listen diligently to me . . . incline your ear
and come to me: hear . . .'[1]*

'Listen to me now, all of you, and understand.'[2]

We live in a very noisy body! It produces a variety of sounds, gaseous rumblings from the alimentary canal, the (usually) soft sounds of gentle breathing or the, often violent, rasping sounds of sleep. However, if we are very quiet, we can sometimes even hear our own heart beating, the valves closing in sequence and the 'swish' of the blood pulsating through the major vessels. One just has to listen.

We can hear the beating heart of another person with our ear over the chest wall; difficult, of course, in such a position to hear one's own heart beating! This act of listening is called immediate auscultation (when performed just with the ear alone) or mediate auscultation with the aid of an instrument, often found around the neck of junior doctors (a kind of badge?) called a stethoscope. This essential instrument was invented in France by the physician Rene Laennec and originally shaped like an old-fashioned ear trumpet. A trained listening ear then remains indispensable for any examining physician; the ear needs to be educated. This technique of listening still provides valuable information about heart function that cannot easily be obtained in any other way.

There are two predominant sounds in each beat of the heart; these arise from the heart valves as they close. Valves, as we have seen, are membranes at the openings between the atria and ventricles and between the ventricles and the major arteries leaving the heart, where their function is to prevent blood flowing back into the heart chambers (regurgitation). These sounds are best heard from the left side of the heart because of the higher pressures generated. The first heart sound, which is also the loudest, is caused by vibrations set up by the sudden closure of these valves at the

---

1   Isaiah 55:2, 3.

2   Mark 7:14 Phillips.

73

commencement of ventricular contraction. This first, crisp sound is low and slightly prolonged (described as 'lub'); the second is shorter and of a higher pitch ('dup'). Sometimes, especially in the young, a third sound can be detected which is soft and low pitched; this coincides with the rapid rush of blood as it flows into the left ventricle. The above is an oversimplification; there are different components to each of these sounds. To listen is crucial.

Further, the ability to hear these sounds depends on the position of the body. This is why, during a physical examination, a patient may be asked to squat, lie flat (supine) and turn to the side. Simply listening to these heart sounds in this way gives valuable information about the health, or otherwise, of the heart. For example, when the heart valves are diseased or incompetent, especially in older people, regurgitation occurs as the blood flows backwards. Such turbulent blood flows are heard, rather like a baby gurgling, as 'murmurs'. In children with a particular congenital defect, such as a hole in the septum between the two ventricles, these 'hole in the heart' murmurs are characteristically pronounced.

As one might imagine the situation is further complicated in pregnancy because when the foetal heart begins to beat there are sounds derived from both hearts. Indeed, detecting the foetal heartbeat is a reassuring confirmation that all is well with the pregnancy itself. Because the foetal heart sounds are quiet, high-pitched and fast (considerably faster than the maternal heart rate) one requires a special stethoscope (called a Pinard tube) or a Doppler probe to detect them. Very musical, indeed rhapsodic, a well syncopated interleaving of the heart beats of the mother and baby. Two rhythms, two lives, within the one body. Even more complicated when there are twins!

There is another simpler way of listening to your heart. A routine visit to the doctor's surgery usually involves meeting up with a clinical nurse and the measurement of your blood pressure. A cuff is placed around the upper arm and then inflated. This obstructs the blood flow to that arm. The pressure in the cuff is then slowly reduced until the outside pressure matches the pressure within the artery. At this point, as the external pressure in the cuff is reduced, just a little blood surges past the constriction producing an audible sound. When first heard this is the highest pressure recorded from the artery and is called the systolic arterial pressure. This 'knocking' sound then continues as the blood is forced through the constriction. As the pressure is lowered further the point is reached when no sound is heard at all; this represents the lowest pressure within the artery and is called the diastolic pressure. The sounds so recorded are reflected down that particular artery from the beating heart; like the soft beat of a drum.

Of course, this is would be a record of blood pressure at one particular time of the day, sitting quietly and perhaps comfortably in the doctor's surgery. It is just one record of pressure at that one time. Throughout the day this pressure varies, with any exercise performed, before and after a meal, or when asleep. The continuous recording of blood pressure during normal daily activities was at one time best achieved using a catheter placed within a suitable artery and the pressure and pulse rate simultaneously recorded on tape. Now, this can be achieved electronically.

Close listening to the heart in the taking of medical history, the cadence of the heart sounds themselves and those valvular murmurs, has parallels to the close listening required for the full enjoyment and appreciation of music, the dynamics, tones, rhythms. Indeed, Michael Field has pointed out that musical notation can be made to represent heart sounds and murmurs both under normal conditions and in disease, such as the opening 'snap' in mitral stenosis as a 'grace note'. The heart makes its own music.

Now, how does all this reflect our own listening to the heart and, more importantly, how does our heart listen to the voices that want to speak to it? We need to listen to ourselves, to others and especially to God.

First, we have to learn to listen to ourselves. Etty Hillesum was a Dutch Jewish student living in enemy-occupied Amsterdam when, in 1941, she started writing a diary of her wartime experiences from her time in the transit camp at Westerbork through to when she was taken to the Nazi concentration camp at Auschwitz. She eventually died there in November 1943. For Etty, 'the most important thing we have to learn in this life' is to listen – and the most important skill, and it is certainly that, is 'to practise the art of listening'. That is the heart of the matter. Etty used the German word 'Hineinhorchen' which means an 'inner listening' to illustrate this. The best word in English would be one which we, not surprisingly, seldom hear today but which comes often in the Bible in the AV version – to 'hearken' to, that is to really listen 'from within', to be attentive to, an awareness of, the voice of the indwelling Christ. 'Truly', Etty said, 'my life is one long listening unto myself, and unto others, unto God'. Interestingly, she then goes on to explain what this means; 'it is really God who hearkens within me'. True. When we believe the promise of Jesus that he will come and make his home within us – in our hearts[3] through the indwelling Spirit, given to 'stand by' us and to be always with us.[4] We have to listen to God living within.

Whereas the 'uncircumcised' heart fails to listen and respond to God's voice[5] the wise man listens[6] and especially to the voice of Jesus. God said of Jesus 'This is my son with whom I am well pleased, listen to him.'[7] We are to listen to his voice.[8] But how in practical terms can we do this? How does God speak to our listening hearts? In two main ways; through his word in Scripture, as we read it in the spirit of prayer and in the silence, but also through that 'inner voice'. How, for example, did Ananias hear the Lord speaking to him 'in a vision'.[9] He could 'hear' a voice and responded with his own ('here I am Lord'). Was this I wonder said aloud? Was it like God's voice to the young Samuel in the Temple?[10] Did it enter his auditory, hearing system? What pathways were used to enter Samuel's mind? This was God speaking 'to the heart'.

Yet, it seems to me that God 'intervenes' in the lives of his people, not only through his written word in the Scriptures but also through quite ordinary things and in everyday ways. Let me illustrate. When we as a family were 'snowed in' during the severe winter of 2018 we could not reach our usual place of worship. I then listened to a broadcast meditation led by the former Bishop of Liverpool, James Jones. In brief, he had come home after cardiac surgery and was drinking soup in his kitchen. No roast beef, or even haggis and neeps, so soon after a serious heart operation! With the spoon halfway between the soup bowl and his mouth God spoke. 'Do not worry. I am with you', words of assurance and comfort. James started to cry with the tears falling into his soup and making it increasingly salty! This was God's voice to his heart, his inner self. And he was listening.

When God speaks to our heart through that inner voice is it just a recollection of Scripture returning to our minds? Or is it through what some would call circumstance or happenchance? For myself, for example,

---

3 John 14:23.

4 John 14:16, 26.

5 Isaiah 6:10.

6 Proverbs 12:15.

7 Matthew 17:5.

8 John 10:16; 18:37.

9 Acts 9:10.

10 1 Samuel 3:4-10.

I have heard God speak to my heart through the alphabet (which led me to both my future wife and to faith in Christ), through a surprise letter from a member of the communist party (a 'blue' letter out of the 'blue'), and through a conversation during an official dinner. So many examples one could give. Give your own! Do such incidents come through coincidence, chance? No! It is God seeking to speak to the heart through such circumstances. The guiding hand has been revealed. The closing of one door only for another, sometimes a quite different door, to be opened. And then the inner conviction of the heart. These changing circumstances become 'sounds' to the heart. Bishop Timothy Dudley-Smith puts it like this: 'Lord of my life, how many things have happened to me that might have happened otherwise?' A mysterious pattern running through life, an overruling Providential guidance revealed by the listening heart. And, there is an important difference between hearing (listening) and seeing. For example, when we read, we can see the ending of that sentence or of that book; we can, if we wish, read backwards and go directly to the last page. With listening we have to wait, we are kept in suspense, because listening is a process extended through time. This why jokes are better heard than read.

These examples involve the Lord speaking to the heart. And, we have to listen and then test to determine whether it is the voice of God.[11] Is it God's Spirit talking to God's Spirit within us?[12] God's Spirit indwells us,[13] he is 'in' our hearts, these are heart sounds! And, often God uses quite 'ordinary' circumstances. We have to 'listen out', sensitive to the Lord's voice. There is participation in the Spirit[14] and this involves a response. Participation includes both listening and responding. Jesus was wonderful at this. Think how he listened to the woman at the well with all her tragic family history, to the blind, to lepers, even – much to the astonishment of the disciples – to children. But especially to his heavenly Father. And, on the Cross Jesus was still listening (to the dying thief) and as he listened, he responded. This is the task of the listening heart. The highest spiritual gift is the ability to listen to the voice of God and to the cries of other people. Like the physician with his stethoscope we need a sensitive ear listening, 'hearkening' carefully to the sounds of the heart within.

---

11 Isaiah 6:8; 1 John 4:1.

12 Galatians 4:6.

13 1 Corinthians 3:16.

14 Philippians 2:1.

M is for THE MUSICAL HEART

'My heart is fixed, O God! I will sing and make music!'[1]
'My servants shall sing for gladness of heart.'[2]
'Singing spiritual songs with thankfulness
in your hearts to God.'[3]

Music permeates God's word from beginning to end, from creation to the end of time. Perhaps the first music in Scripture comes in the Garden of Eden when Adam and Eve 'heard the voice of the Lord God walking in the garden in the cool (the Hebrew is 'wind') of the day among the trees'.[4] The music of the wind in the trees, the Lord singing ('the voice') or the music, the rhythm of the Lord's footsteps? And, Scripture closes with music; trumpets and the sound of thousands of voices singing the praise of God Almighty. No wonder then that for those who believe music is an integral part of who we are.

One of the most important events in my life as an early teenager was my mother's desire that I should learn the piano. This was an added financial expense for what was already a poor household; my mother worked in the local primary school as a 'dinner lady' as that position was then called – now the term used for such a position is 'chef'! Today some well-known ones are now working in schools to improve the diet of young people. My father always had two jobs, and sometimes had a third to 'make ends meet'. So, to pay for music lessons for myself and my younger brother (violin, viola) was no light added burden on the family finances. I was very fortunate in that my piano teacher had been a pupil and friend of the great Dame Myra Hess and I can remember being invited to meet the great lady, introduced by my teacher, during the interval of one of Dame Myra's concerts in the Royal Albert Hall in London. In those days it was usual, almost unknown

---

1   Psalm 57:7.
2   Isaiah 65:14.
3   Colossians 3:16.
4   Genesis 3:8.

today, for a soloist to play two major piano concertos in the one concert; one before and one after the interval with a change of dress for the second concerto! This was certainly true of Dame Myra and also, most notably, of another lady pianist the flamboyant Australian Eileen Joyce. My teacher suggested, with my assent, that I should not go down the usual route of exams but play simply for enjoyment. Wonderful decision! Flat residents permitting, perhaps piano playing is still earmarked for part of whatever is left of the future.

These experiences led me to explore other music. We had a small battery-operated radio on which I found I could receive the then equivalent of today's BBC Radio 3, discovering for the first time the symphonies of Mozart, Beethoven and especially Bruckner and Dvorak. Haydn, now my favourite, came later. Being at that time resident in London I, with my brother, often went to the Promenade Concerts at the Royal Albert Hall and later at the Festival Hall on the South Bank built for the Festival of Britain in 1951. I saw all the great pianists of that time (such as Solomon, Curzon, Moiseiwitsch, Edwin Fischer) and conductors, including Furtwangler and Toscanini, as well as those conductors responsible for the BBC Proms; just three conductors in those days – Boult, Sargent and Cameron and the one orchestra. Some task to undertake to conduct so many Prom concerts night after night; for the 2019 Proms there are more than fifty conductors sharing the podium and many orchestras! So, music and these experiences of both playing, listening and watching, became one of the most formative experiences of my life. So much pleasure! Is musical appreciation a gift from God? I think it is. 'The precious music of the heart', as Wordsworth wrote.

Our normal heart rate is regular, consistent and is around sixty to seventy beats each minute, say roughly one each second. Similar to the rate of the slow movement of Mahler's first symphony (the 'Frere Jacques' theme), Chopin's 'Raindrop' Prelude or, although the rhythm is somewhat different, the slow movement of Beethoven's third (*Eroica*) symphony. The heart rate is slower during sleep but considerably faster during exercise or excitement – and during listening to some music! These rate changes are due, in the main, to the activity of the autonomic (sympathetic) nerves which supply the heart. This increase in sympathetic drive occurs during exercise, anxiety (those few seconds before having to speak in public) and during listening to 'exciting' music. These changes in heart rate are determined centrally, responding to outside influences or to inner tensions. It would be fascinating to measure the heart rate of performers and members of the audience during a normal symphonic (or pop) concert. Now certainly possible.

The heart is a very musical organ. With the heart, as in music, there are changes both in rate and rhythm. Both are inherent properties of cardiac muscle; it is the pacemaker situated in the heart itself (in the sinoatrial node) that determines both. Normal cardiac rhythm begins at the node before being propagated as a wave through the atria and then the ventricles along specially adapted cardiac muscle fibres, the electrical signals involved being picked up in the electrocardiogram.

In music the essential characteristic is the 'beat'. This too varies in rate; fast, very fast, fairly slow – at walking pace – slow, very slow (allegro, presto, andante, largo, lento); it depends on the metronome markings (if any) set by the composer – or by the conductor: the rate has been known to be determined by the time required for the conductor to catch a train or plane immediately after the concert. There are changes not only in rate but also in rhythm. Think of the rhythm of a Strauss waltz, or Ravel's Bolero (which the composer himself described as 'orchestral tissue without music'!) or the martial theme in the first movement of the Shostakovich 'Leningrad' symphony. So many examples and variations. Fortunately, the rhythm of the heart is fairly consistent. Marked changes could be dangerous.

The Australian doctor Michael Field wrote a letter to the medical journal The Lancet in 2010 on the rhythms of music and their relation to the biological rhythms of the heart. Field suggested a specific role of music in teaching medical students the rudiments of cardiac auscultation; the skills involved in attentive listening to the heart during the taking of a medical history parallel the close listening involved in listening to music. He was particularly interested in the 'music' of heart sounds, those associated with the rumbling qualities of the heart murmurs, such as regurgitation, a sound that occurs with stenosis of the heart valves, or even the dying away (decrescendo) of aortic regurgitation. One can link this particular sound with the 'dying away' (morendo) at the end of, for example, Vaughan Williams second and fifth symphonies. Indeed, Beethoven set his own cardiac rhythm disturbance to music in his Piano Sonata opus 81a which he called 'Les adieux'.

This was long before Einthoven documented graphically the electrical expression of regular or irregular cardiac activity in the form of the electrocardiogram but certainly centuries after the ancient (fifth century BC) Chinese 'pulse theory', which suggested a link between the pulse, as recorded from the wrist, and the sounds of 'strings and tones'.

What effect does music have on the heart rate and rhythm? Of course, in music there are powerful changes in emotion and mood and these are also associated with changes in heart rate, blood pressure and respiratory rate. 'Exciting music' leads to an increase in sympathetic discharge and increases in heart rate and blood pressure; when this response is intense (musical frisson) there are also 'shivers', 'goosepimples', and piloerection; that is, the 'hairs of the head, and of other parts of the body, stand on end', effects resulting from increased sympathetic activity. There are also changes in the electrical activity of the heart as recorded from the electrocardiogram; an increase in the amplitude of the QRS complex for example.

It would be interesting if the pulse rate of orchestral and choral conductors could be monitored during a concert. It is said that the heart rate of the conductor Herbert von Karajan when conducting Beethoven's Leonore No. 3 was higher than when he was landing his personal jet aircraft! This heart response to music is thankfully not lost in old age; indeed, perhaps with age response to music becomes even more 'from the heart' and more emotional. And, at the other end of life's scale when does music first influence us? It seems that perception of music begins early; aural learning begins 'in utero', it is a pre-natal experience to music, the foetal heart rate responds to music heard or sung by the mother. 'Sweet music' played to, or by, the mother during pregnancy is said to 'mould' the baby's temperament. Many great composers, Mozart and Dvorak for example, grew up in an environment surrounded by music – even in the womb. However fortunately, increases in heart rate do not follow the musical beat. Otherwise we would see more cases of sudden cardiac death in our concert halls or on the conductor's rostrum. It has been known to happen: music can be an exciting – and sometimes dangerous pursuit.

In contrast, quiet and slow music has the opposite effect and can be associated with decreases in both heart rate and blood pressure. These result from an increase in vagal (parasympathetic activity) and a decrease in sympathetic activity. In patients with heart disease (and also with cancer) there is also a reduction in anxiety and pain and an improvement in the quality of sleep ('music assisted relaxation'). Music is potentially a low-cost and safe adjuvant for intervention and therapy! Music with a repetitive 10-second cycle has a noticeable calming effect because, as Professor Peter Sleight of Oxford University has pointed out, this matches the normal control rhythm of the cardiovascular system. And, according to a report from the American Society of Hypertension, listening to just 30 minutes of classical music a day results in a significant reduction in blood pressure and heart rate – a safe, effective, non-pharmacological treatment. Beta-hoven blockers twice a day! My own experience bears this out. Before a particular surgical operation, I was told to take a cassette into theatre with suitable music of my choice (some surgeons are known to insist on choosing their own). My choice was a Mozart piano concerto. This was not only to calm me during the surgical procedures but also to cut out the noise – in my case of surgical banging and sawing!

Before leaving this subject perhaps a word or two about drugs and musical performance. We have seen that the calming effects of music involve a combination of an increase in vagal tone (which slows the heart rate) and a decrease in sympathetic drive, which has a similar effect. These effects are mediated centrally via the brain. Slowing the heart also results from blocking the sympathetic end-receptor (called beta-adrenoceptors) and for which the Scottish pharmacologist 'Jimmy' Black won the Nobel Prize for Medicine. These drugs, called 'beta-blockers', are used clinically both to reduce blood pressure and, by slowing the heart and reducing contractile strength, the oxygen requirements of 'pounding' hearts. They also reduce tremor. In the United States some orchestral string players and soloists have been known to take beta-blockers (obtained illicitly) to reduce unnecessary vibrato. Some music students have been known to use them to still their nerves prior to an important examination; 'taking them prior to an audition is as normal as getting your instrument out of the case' said one. A replacement then for alcohol or, in the case of the great violinist Yehudi Menuhin, bananas. The reason for this 'banana therapy' could be its high potassium content; potassium is known to slow the heart and in high doses stop it completely. So, no more than one banana prior to that important performance!

The calming, therapeutic effect of music is mediated from the brain where the chemical linked to this effect is probably dopamine, described as the 'reward or pleasure chemical', this also 'governs' sympathetic discharge and so controls responses such as heart rate, skin conductance (hence those 'goose pimples') and the rate of breathing. This fascinating subject of 'mind and music' is somewhat outwith our present scope but a good introduction, including a survey of music in therapy and its apparent mind-boosting, IQ increasing, spatial awareness improving effect (sometimes referred to as the 'Mozart Effect') can be found in Oliver Sacks' book, *Musicophilia: Tales of Music and the Brain*. First published in 2007 and still very much in print.

We have said nothing yet about sound; how loud or how 'soft' the music is and what effect that has on the human heart. Or, no sound at all. Silence. Silence is often a neglected ingredient of music. Not that pause in the music for the sake of effect, which is out of place (and when it sometimes feels as though the conductor has 'lost the place') but that subtle 'silence of anticipation'. The example comes to mind of the two second silence after the climax in the slow movement of Schubert's 'Great' C major symphony which is then followed by quietly plucked string chords. Or the silence before the music starts (the anticipation of what is so soon to come) or the 'silence of appreciation' that hush that comes at the end of great music when the audience is so affected that applause seems superfluous. Such a silence can even come at end of a message from God's word when the Lord has really spoken. When silence is indeed golden.

There is another factor that can make the heart almost stop, although fortunately this never really happens! This is when there is a sudden, unexpected change of key, from major to minor for example. This so called 'deceptive cadence' is the real essence of music and really 'gets to the heart'; one expects a certain repeated chord sequence and, just when we expect it again, the composer changes the last chord to one that is unexpected. This was a favourite 'trick' of Haydn and especially Schubert. I was reminded of this 'heart stopping' effect a couple of months ago when listening with my wife to a piano recital in Dunblane Cathedral. The pianists were the husband and wife duo of James Willshire and Pippa Harrison and the moment was the sudden change of key at the very end of Schubert's Fantasia in F minor (D940) for piano duo. Incidentally, this gifted couple have a desire to link, in their recitals, music with their Christian faith through their 'Christians Musicians Collective' which has the 'aim of combining the glorious news of Jesus Christ with classical music of the highest calibre in concert or church settings'.

There is a mysterious power that music wields over many people and this emotional response can be intense. Of great joy (such as Bach's Magnificat), or of dread (fear even) calm or of tremendous excitement. Opera, being both aural and visual is particularly effective. Think of that sound generated by a heroic tenor in operas such as Verdi's, Don Carlos or Puccini's, La Boheme causing many hearts, especially perhaps female hearts, to 'flutter'. Or that marvellous aural spectacle generated by the Queen of the Night's aria in Mozart's *Magic Flute*. Even more spine tickling is Zerbinetta's coloratura aria in Richard Strauss' *Ariadne auf Naxos*, vulnerability and flightiness shining through. Or, in the same opera, Ariadne's 'death aria' with its vaunting lines, shiver-inducing harmonies and impossibly lush climaxes, the ancestor of a thousand Hollywood soundtracks. So much of music speaks to the heart or, as Beethoven put it, 'music of the heart that speaks to the heart'. The Italian composer Donizetti said, as he wrote his comic opera *L'elisir d'amore*, 'the heart speaks, the head reaches forward and the hand writes'. Whilst it was said of Rachmaninov, when conducting Tchaikovsky's opera, *Queen of Spades*, 'he explored the heart and essence of the piece because he apparently identified with it so deeply'. Exploration by the heart of the music of the heart.

Now, if this is true of music in general how much more of religious music! The Bible is permeated by music from beginning to end, from the song of Miriam and Moses' song to the Lord, after the Lord had saved Israel from the hands of the Egyptians,[5] to the repeated songs in heaven in the book of Revelation. These are examples of songs of praise and worship; thanksgiving and praise in the Exodus song – 'I will sing to the Lord for he has triumphed gloriously', 'The Lord is my strength and song and is become my salvation' or 'Who is like you, O Lord'. This is a personal song to the Lord – 'I will sing'. Whereas in the heavenly songs in Revelation it is praise pure and simple sung by thousands – 'Holy is the Lord God Almighty', 'Worthy are you, our Lord and God to receive . . .' Corporate singing by thousands, thrilling even to read about. How much more thrilling to hear it sung!

Music has long been a prominent feature of church services and there are clear scriptural warrants for this. Of course, the words of such hymns and songs are to God himself; they are of praise, worship and thanksgiving. We are to make melody in our hearts to the Lord and it is true that the

---

5 Exodus 15:1-21.

words of well-loved hymns stay long in the memory just as do the words of Scripture, memories ingrained in the brain's hard drive. But we sing not only to the Lord but to one another. Paul and Silas in prison sang to the Lord but also to the other prisoners and Paul in his letters says we are to sing to one another.[6] This encourages. Good to look at the faces of fellow worshipers as we ourselves sing. Hopefully we see there the joy of the Lord! My wife and I now go each fortnight to a 'lunch break' for those of a certain age. Around fifty folk are present. We always close with the song 'May God's blessing surround you each day' and, as we do so we look around at one another, for it is both a prayer to God and a word of encouragement to each other as we part.

Of course, the centre of music in the Bible is the 'book' of Psalms. These psalms were of course written for singing, they are the oxygen of corporate worship. How many of those attributed to David himself, or written for him, begin with instructions to the 'choirmaster', sometimes telling him (or her?) which musical instruments should be used to accompany the songs, 'strings' (*neginoth*) 'the music of strings makes me glad'[7] or to be plucked – like a harp (as in Psalms 54 and 55). Some needed the accompaniment of flutes, trumpets, horns, pipes (of the bagpipe kind I wonder?) and percussion. The introductions to some of the psalms seem to suggest the tunes to which they could be sung – 'according to the dove', or 'far-off terebinths' (the turpentine tree), 'dove of the dawn' (which must have been a lovely, calming 'tune'), 'according to lilies' or 'do not destroy' (do not lose?). One (Psalm 88) gives the author of the text (Heman the Ezrahite) as well as the tune it is to be sung to: the copyright in this case seemingly held by the worship leader himself.

(The subject of hymns, so many of which come from, and go to, the heart, is outwith the present scope but those interested in the art of hymn writing could well begin with Timothy Dudley-Smith's book, *A Functional Art: Reflections of a Hymn Writer*', published in 2017 by Oxford University Press.)

One wonders if the choirmaster gave adequate time for rehearsal for the singing of these psalms or, as sometimes happens with church services today, was it all at the last minute? Were rehearsals even needed? Did the conductor, the chief musician, 'lead from the front', like a precentor? And,

---

6   Ephesians 5:19, Colossians 3:16.
7   Psalm 45:8.

as for the music itself, that would depend on the context of that particular psalm, the background sometimes elaborated specifically at the head of each. Good examples are those to psalm 51 (written when 'Nathan the prophet went to him after he had gone into Bathsheba', surely then with a very solemn accompaniment), or Psalms 52, 54, 56, 57 and 59, all probably written when David was 'on the run' from King Saul.

The other instruction for the choirmaster was the kind of setting; most of these terms (*miktam, maschil*) were probably musical terms, some apparently well known. For example, are the words 'do not destroy' (at the head of Psalms 57–59), the name of a set tune or did the words mean simply 'keep this safe' for use on another occasion? The essential thing however is that these psalms were meant to be sung, expressing the whole gamut of experiences and situations. Hence their relevance for today. They are 'prayer songs' often songs of great leaping, overflowing joy. As Pamela Goldberg[8] writes in the introduction to her new translation of the psalms:

> These are poems not to formulate religious doctrine, but to give voice (note!) to all emotion, from anguish to exaltation, loneliness to thanksgiving, yearning to rage. Where our hearts go, the psalms sing with us.

Perhaps the most interesting of these words of direction, coming over 70 times in the psalms, is *Selah*. What does this word mean, so often found along that right-hand margin? Almost certainly a musical term, coming at significant places and probably meaning 'more emphasis here', or 'draw attention to these words', sing more loudly (crescendo), 'highlight or pause here' (a moment of silent reflection), 'really sing from the heart here', or does this intriguing word simply mean 'think on't' – 'what do you think about that!' One can imagine the expression and the body movements of the choral conductor at these points! *Selah*!

But, how often are psalms now sung? They certainly were fifty years ago; part of almost every Church of Scotland service. Today they seem to be restricted to certain denominations and places and, unlike in their original setting, without instruments.

There is one other example of music in the Old Testament used for a rather different but specific purpose. That is where the young David,

---

8   *The Complete Psalms*, the book of prayer songs in a new translation by Pamela Goldberg, Bloomsbury, London 2010.

with his gifts in poetry and music, was called upon to play his lyre for King Saul.[9] The purpose was to calm the king's nervous and excitable temperament, his incurable melancholy, his tendency to depression and gloom, to morbid suspicion and violent impulses. This 'therapy' was successful; 'whenever David took the lyre and played it with his hand Saul was refreshed and was well; the harmful spirit departed from him'. Saul then was clearly affected by music: earlier the songs and chants of the pupils of the prophetic schools had had a powerful influence over the king.[10] In this case music was to have a quite different effect, rather than calming it resulted in excitable prophecy – the Spirit of God came upon him. A glimpse perhaps of one of the effects of music on some present-day congregations at worship?

So far, we have thought about the effect of music on the 'heart'. Are there instances of the heart's own music, it's beat, having an influence on musical composition? Attempts to replicate heart sounds in musical terms. I think there are. J.S. Bach saw God in everything he wrote and there are clear correlations between extracts of his music and the Bible. The pianist Frederico Coli has pointed out how, in the great Chaconne, the concluding movement of his D minor Partita for solo violin, the accent is on the second beat of the bar, like someone walking with a limp, like Jacob:[11] 'Here, in this music, we are in the presence of Jacob'.

A particularly good example of this comes in Haydn's *Seven Last Words of Our Saviour on the Cross*, of which there are several versions – for orchestra with and without choir, for string quartet, even for piano. This work has an interesting background. In 1785 Haydn received an invitation from the Archbishop of Cadiz to write an instrumental composition, to be divided into seven short orchestral sections and conceived so as to fit the seven last words from the Cross. These were to be played between the archbishop's own comments on these words at a Good Friday service and as he was praying at the altar. To compose these 'interludes of prayer' was no mean task. It was no easy matter Haydn said, 'to compose seven adagios lasting ten minutes each without causing fatigue in the listeners'. Yet he wanted his composition to be readily understandable in order to be sure of the effect 'from heart to heart'. It is in response to the first of these seven

---

9   1 Samuel 16:14–23.

10   1 Samuel 10:5, 6.

11   Genesis 32:25, 31.

words, 'Father forgive them for they do not know what they do', that under the melody in the first violin (in the string quartet version of the work) there is the tread of the lower strings at the tempo of a normal heart beat. Later, in response to the last word ('Father into your hands I commend my spirit') the underlying beat quickens, as it does towards the end of life, and then there is a 'heart stop', a silence, before the final note. Haydn, who was a devout believer, had a particular love for this composition which illustrates so dramatically the story of the Passion. Perhaps the nearest even he ever got to achieving music that spoke 'from heart to heart'.

N is for the NOURISHED HEART

'The whole body, having nourishment increases with the increase of God.'[1]

'They received the word with all readiness and searched the scriptures daily.'[2]

Like every other part of the body the heart needs an adequate supply of energy in order to perform its function of pumping five or six litres of blood every minute. Although some of the nutrients required for this energy expenditure can be stored within the heart muscle, this is limited and certainly oxygen cannot be stored. This means that heart muscle cannot tolerate an interruption of its blood (oxygen) supply for long periods. This supply of blood comes from two large arteries (the right and left coronary arteries) which are the first branches of the aorta; about 5% of the output of the heart goes into these arteries. The left coronary artery divides, soon after its point of origin, into the circumflex and anterior descending arteries which supply the mass of the left ventricle. The right coronary artery supplies not only the right ventricle but part of the rear of the left side of the heart. Both these main coronary arteries are superficial, lying on the surface of the heart. They are well visible in the drawing of the heart by Leonardo de Vinci shown at the beginning of the book.

There is a marvellous and precise relationship between the demands of the heart for oxygen and nutrients and the supply of blood to match these demands through the coronary circulation. This demand/supply relation, and how this is regulated, is one of the many marvels of the blood circulation to the heart. For example, the increase in cardiac work during exercise, when the output from the heart can reach over twenty or more litres every minute (even a five to six-fold increase in severe exercise) is perfectly matched under physiological conditions by the increase in coronary blood

---

1 Colossians 2:19.

2 Acts 17:11.

flow; demand is balanced by supply. How this coupled balance is regulated, fascinating though it is, lies outwith the scope of this chapter but basically it means that the heart (the user) communicates ('talks') to its supplier (the coronary vessels). 'More nutrients are required, please supply'! Because the demand comes first, the heart muscle must have the ability to 'talk back' to the vessels supplying it with its energy requirements. How this 'talking' is achieved has fascinated those physiologists involved in research on the coronary circulation, including the present author, for many years.

What nutrients are required by the working heart? First, and crucial, is oxygen which is needed for the (aerobic) metabolism required to release the energy necessary for the heart to contract. For example, there is a precise, and linear, relationship between this oxygen demand and the oxygen consumed both under resting conditions and during situations when the heart has to beat more frequently and more strongly such as during exertion. For this metabolic fuel the heart can utilise a whole variety of substances such as glucose and fatty acids.

If there are any engineers reading this they may well be puzzled by the question as to how, if the main supplying channels are situated on the surface of the heart, blood reaches the deeper parts of the heart when it has to traverse a considerable mass of forcibly contracting muscle? The answer is that there are main vessels penetrating the muscle mass (many centimetres thick) at right angles to the main arteries, to reach the inner parts of the ventricles. However, these vessels are closed during systole by the contracting muscle pressing, clenching on them from outside. This means that blood can only reach the vessels in the deeper parts of the heart (known as the subendocardial plexus) when the heart is relaxed, that is during diastole. This is easily observed when coronary flow is measured during the whole cardiac cycle.

We should now raise another question, which was earlier touched on and will be discussed later under 'S – protection (salvation) of the heart against damage'. This question concerns 'new' coronary vessels, how they are formed and how they grow. This process is called angiogenesis. These vessels become useful, and in some cases are vital, in supplying blood to the heart when it is under attack. Let us return to the illustration of a blocked main road. If a road is completely blocked, after an accident for example, then the road beyond that blocked portion will be empty of traffic. Unless that is, there are other roads entering beyond (distal to) the obstruction from a different road system. In the circulation these vessels entering the blocked artery downstream from an obstruction are known as collaterals. These can develop in all places where they are needed but with a preference for the subendocardial plexus, that is, the deep places of the heart. This fascinating subject of 'new vessels for old' is well discussed in a book edited by Jutta and Wolfgang Schaper[3] and which has more general implications for the cardiovascular system.

Some of these collaterals are not 'new'; new in the sense that they are only formed (and their growth greatly enhanced) under conditions where a major artery is narrowed and then blocked. These vessels may well have been already there in the form of communicating channels, called collaterals, between the main coronary arteries. Indeed, people of middle-age may already have a reasonably well-developed collateral circulation to counteract the damaging effects of the potential block of a major artery. They hence become part of the heart's defence system against possible attack. Such vessels may be the remnants of those present in the foetal heart and their presence in some patients could be regarded as fortunate but not fortuitous.

Some years ago I visited an old friend in hospital who had had a heart attack due to an occluded coronary artery. When I arrived at the hospital he was in theatre having an angioplasty to break up the occlusion and to insert a stent. The cardiologist knew me and invited me to observe the procedure. Fortunately, the area of the heart once supplied by the blocked artery was receiving blood from another artery from the same vessel but above the occlusion site so my friend had a quite good additional collateral circulation; this new vessel had grown by the process of angiogenesis in response to the gradually developing occlusion. Fortunate, because without this newly formed coronary artery the result may well have been catastrophic.

Just as cardiac muscle cells, and the functioning of the heart as a pump, depend on a regular and constant blood supply, so too our spiritual heart needs a constant and regular diet of spiritual food. And, just as an uneven, severely reduced coronary blood flow results in cardiac impairment (since the heart cannot function without the oxygen provided by it) so too the spiritual heart is in need of God's word – its spiritual food. Without it there would be, as in the physical realm, pain, impairment of spiritual function and ultimately disaster. This emphasises the need for the regular, suitable and constant provision of spiritual food; 'man shall not live by bread alone but by every word that proceeds from the mouth of God'.[4] 'Give us our daily bread' is the

---

3   W and J Schaper ed., *Arteriogenesis*, Kluwer Academic, Dordrecht 2004.
4   Matthew 4:4; Luke 4:4.

cry of the hungry human heart. Indeed, this phrase 'daily bread' is the title of a number of books of Bible readings enabling us to be regularly fed. And, just as for our physical health we have regular, set times for our meals, usually three times each day, so too we need to set aside regular times for our spiritual bread. The question is when and how should this be done. As to the when, many Christians find the morning the most appropriate time. This enables us to 'take' God's word with us into the rest of the normal working day. It means we continue to 'digest' or masticate God's word, feeding on it, returning to it and allowing it 'to dwell in our heart' and become part of us. So, what are the practical out-workings of this? What follows is the very simple, basic routine I have tried to follow, not always successfully, in over sixty years of attempting to follow Christ. Of course, it will not be suitable for everyone.

First, to return to the coronary blood flow analogy, it has to be regular. At least daily, helpfully at set times. The example of the Christians in Berea is a good one.[5] Then, not only regular but continuing. Any breakdown in the blood supply to the heart is damaging; so too with our spiritual food.

Second, the reading needs to be bathed in prayer. It is only the Holy Spirit that can help us to understand and then apply God's word to our individual lives. We need to be open to what God is saying to us. It is a living word through which we hear God. This must come to us in a relaxed, expectant atmosphere, just as the maximum blood supply to the heart comes at the relaxed (diastolic) phase of the cardiac cycle. The prayer life of Jesus shows us that, when he was in communication with his Father, he 'retreated' to quiet places.[6] He advised others to do the same.[7]

Last, and here the analogy breaks down (at least partially) there should be variety in the way this spiritual food is provided. Same food (God's word) but variety in the way it comes to us. Thankfully, not all meals are the same! Variety then. Just as the coronary blood flow is varied in the way it is controlled; there are metabolic, neural and mechanical factors involved in this control but no single mechanism. Flow too is dependent upon what the heart requires, more energy expenditure, more flow to meet these increased requirements. Was it not at the many critical times in Jesus' ministry that his times of prayer were more evident?[8] Are there not times when we need even more nutritious food

---

5   Acts 17:11.

6   Mark 6:46; Luke 9:18; 11:1.

7   Matthew 6:6.

8   Luke 9:28; 22:41, 44.

as our spiritual needs increase, in special times of service for example? After all, when our physical heart is especially 'busy' it needs substantial increases in that nourishing blood flow, so too in times of spiritual need or service we need more time with God in prayer and in the word. Certainly not less.

I look back over the past year or so and give examples of the varied spiritual food I have found helpful. Here they are!

Ways of trekking through the Bible in a year or two. Those I have used include John Stott: *Daily Reflections from Genesis to Revelation*, using 'the church year'[9] and by Don Carson *For the Love of God*, 'a daily companion for discovering the riches of God's Word'.[10] This takes the whole Bible over a two year period and is in two volumes. *The One Year Bible*[11] is 'the entire Bible arranged in 365 daily readings' but has no comments on the verses.

As Kingfishers Catch Fire, by Eugene Peterson[12] and *Someone Who Beckons* by Timothy Dudley-Smith.[13] Two wonderful books that I have used as daily readings twice annually for the past couple of years. Strongly recommended!

A Private House of Prayer, by Leslie D. Weatherhead.[14] This, as the name suggests, is mainly a book on prayer with a linked Bible passage for each day of the month. I now read this about four times a year. It never dates and is for me indispensable. I have three well used copies!

Some commentaries are helpful for daily Bible reading. One of my friends has used the *Daily Study Bible* (New Testament commentaries) of William Barclay[15] as daily readings for several years. Commentaries I have found helpful for daily devotions are listed at the end of the book. The key word here is 'varied'!

Scripture Union and the Bible Reading Fellowship have published 'daily notes' for many years. These remain the staple spiritual diet of many Christians. But, also try some of the above!

---

9 Published by Candle Books, 2006.

10 Intervarsity Press, 1988.

11 Kingsway Publications.

12 Hodder and Stoughton, 2017.

13 Hodder and Stoughton, 1994.

14 Hodder and Stoughton, 1958 but reprinted since, the last in 1999.

15 Published by Saint Andrew Press, Edinburgh (varied dates; the original rather than the revised editions are best).

O is for the OPEN HEART

'Having the eyes of your heart open...'[1]

Open, 'any vacant or unobstructed space, a passage, a word that means allowing freedom of access'. True of doors, of minds (although not so open that they keep nothing in or out), open eyes, for example worshipping with open eyes[2] and, in the present context, open hearts.

I was in Hungary in 1989 when the government opened the border with Austria thus allowing the citizens of the DDR (East Germany) free passage to 'go west'; the border between Hungary and the DDR was always open, both being members of the communist bloc. I was also present in Hungary later when the Berlin Wall came down (much celebrating in the Department in which I then worked) leading to the unification of Germany. I had many friends in 'the east' and made many visits behind the 'iron curtain', sometimes a rather scary experience. I remember one of my friends in East Berlin getting into his Trabant car (said, by some, to be made of cardboard) and driving with his son to visit his mother in West Berlin on the day the wall came down, the first time his son had met his granny. So, open means accessibility. As we shall see, this is true both of the physical heart (and mind) and of the spiritual heart. Open to God. Two-way traffic. We are to be open to God and God open to us.

Now 'open the chest' said the surgeon. This in order to reach the heart. Tens of thousands of people have heart surgery in Britain each year and whereas one patient in ten died after open-chest cardiac surgery in the 1970's now, despite it still being major surgery, the mortality from such operations is very much less than one in a hundred. The most common kinds of heart surgery are coronary artery bypass graft surgery (to replace blocked coronary arteries with a 'donor' part of an artery or vein from another part of the body), heart valve surgery (repair or replacement) and, in infants and children, surgery to correct a congenital defect. There is a fascinating book

---

1   Ephesians 1:18.
2   John 4:23.

on children with congenital heart disease by Max Gerber called 'My heart in the real world'. Transplantation surgery is discussed elsewhere (under T).

Major heart surgery requires that the chest is opened and held open with retractors. Traditionally this means sectioning one or more of the ribs in order to reach the heart, although sometimes it can be accessed through sectioning the side wall of the chest; the chest bone is then not cut completely. This is called 'minimal access surgery'. Even so, the chest has to be opened and the surgeon needs to see what he is doing. Of course, if you are the patient, you cannot feel or hear any of this because in the anaesthetic room the anaesthetist has inserted a catheter into a suitable vein and given something (an intravenous anaesthetic) to send you into the land of Nod. Interestingly as the chest is opened there is a smell, musky, like half-clean breath. In addition to the direct visual field, an ultrasound camera is sometimes placed in the gullet (oesophagus) to give additional information about how the heart is doing.

Because it is easier to operate on the heart when it is quiescent (non-beating, still) the heart needs to be stopped and the blood diverted to a heart-lung machine, an artificial pump, which takes over the normal pumping role of the heart whilst the operation is proceeding. It does sometimes happen that stopping the heart may not be required since the surgery can be performed whilst the heart is still beating. This is called 'off-pump' surgery. A moving experience!

Now, a little history. Michael E. DeBakey was the pioneer surgeon who in the early 1930s built a pump (the so called 'roller pump') to deliver blood from a donor to a patient. His team was, in 1968 the first to use four organs (heart, kidneys, leg) from one donor and given to several recipients. He once wrote 'The role of Providence in human endeavour is speculative but purposeful'. It is of interest that his own life was saved by a procedure he himself had devised.

For any heart operation there needs to be preparation. For the surgeon and his team this requires very many years of learning and experience. Preparation is also needed for the patient following the recommendation that cardiac surgery is required. In the weeks before surgery he or she needs to keep healthy, perhaps losing weight, and pay a visit to the dentist, because infected teeth or gums can introduce bacteria into the blood stream. Then there are pre-operative assessments requiring a battery of tests, blood sampling (including knowledge of the relevant blood group to replace blood loss during the operation), electrocardiographic recordings to assess cardiac function, preparation of skin and hair and premedication prior to administration of the anaesthetic. The essential point then is that thought and preparation are very important before open-heart surgery. There are spiritual implications in such careful preparation.

There are three spiritual perspectives to consider. First, God opens his heart to us. For example, by his word, as the Emmaus road disciples discovered, 'did not our hearts burn within us as he (Jesus) opened to us the Scriptures'.[3] Jesus opened their minds, 'their understanding'. Second, we ourselves need to be open to God. Third, we are to be open to others.

First then, God is the one who 'opens' his heart to us. And, not only his heart; his hands too are also open[4] – in generosity. On earth Jesus opened blind eyes and spiritually does the same to our spiritual eyes today. Then Paul thanked God for the opportunities for the furtherance of the gospel, 'open for utterance'.[5] He prayed for God to enable him to open God's word in order for him to speak it, as had the psalmist centuries earlier, 'open my lips'.[6] He asked that God would 'open' even more doors in order to give him more opportunities to proclaim the gospel.[7] We too pray for God to give to us understanding of his word, 'open my eyes'[8] before we ourselves open the Scriptures. Elisha prayed, in a seemingly desperate situation, for his servant to see 'beyond sight' – 'open his eyes' he prayed.[9] And, it was when Jesus broke the bread that the two Emmaus disciples had their eyes opened to see, to understand who he was.[10]

Second, we need to be open with God, to 'tell all we know'. Open hearts. This is to risk exposure, it is to acknowledge our faults, the real truth about ourselves even though God knows our hearts anyway. As Francis Havergal wrote, 'no words shall needed be, Thou knowest all so well'. 'You are familiar with all my ways, you have searched me and known me'.[11] Known completely.

3 Luke 24:32.
4 Psalm 145:16.
5 1 Corinthians 16:9.
6 Psalm 51:15.
7 Colossians 4:3.
8 Psalm 119:18.
9 2 Kings 6:17.
10 Luke 24:31.
11 Psalm 139:1.

In religious terms to be open with God means confession. Are there tracts, areas in our lives into which God is not allowed to enter? The 'deep' places in our lives we want to 'keep' from God, playing roles that serve to conceal one's true nature, masking the whole truth about ourselves. To be open to God means to have nothing closed off, nothing in our hearts and minds that does not allow him access. It means free flow, back and forth, freedom of movement, no barriers of any kind. As with the heart there is 'beauty in openness'.

This openness involves confession since, to approach God in prayer, there must be no barriers, no obstructions on our side. There are no such barriers on God's side; he is open to receive our praise and petitions but since 'God is of purer eyes than to behold iniquity, he cannot look on wrong',[12] barriers on our side need to be removed. This, of course, was the reason for the provision in the Old Testament of sacrifices in order to admit guilt, to cleanse from sin and thus make the way for the people to come into God's presence. Confession then means to admit our shortcomings, to acknowledge, albeit often with some reluctance, the truth of our spiritual condition before him. That we have 'sinned in thought, word and deed', admitting the evil we have done 'and the good we have not done, through ignorance, through weakness through our own deliberate fault'. As Archbishop Thomas Cranmer has it in the 1553 Communion Service we come to God 'not weighing our merits, not trusting in our own righteousness but trusting in God's manifold (various, many) and great mercies', believing that 'God is willing to pardon our offences through Jesus Christ'. In Samuel Davies' wonderful hymn 'Great God of wonders' are the words, 'In wonder lost, with trembling joy, we take the pardon of our God, pardon for sins of deepest dye, a pardon sealed with Jesus blood'. We need to be open. 'Hidden except to God alone, not seen by others – angel seemed to human sight, stood a leper in Thy light'. Or this:

'Sins unnumbered I confess, of exceeding sinfulness. Sins against Thyself alone, only to omniscience known'. Are we ashamed to open our sinful hearts to God? 'Let not my many failures make me too ashamed to come any more; that would be ultimate darkness'.

The classic confession of sin from an open heart in Scripture comes in Psalm 51. The story of David and Bathsheba, which prompted this confession and which unravels in 2 Samuel (chapters 11 and 12), concerns David's adultery with Bathsheba and the arranged murder of her husband,

---

12 Habakkuk 1:13.

the faithful Uriah. The first thing David had to do was to open his heart and admit his sin[13] because it is 'ever before him',[14] it confronts him continually. This is David acknowledging, admitting openly his sin, appreciating the holiness of God – 'against thee only have I sinned'. This is sin stemming from the 'inner part'. Yet David longs to be right with God. As Blaiklock has well said 'sin begins in the hidden depths of the mind, the depths of the corrupted heart' and it is there, in the secret place, that the remedy must begin. The heart has to be opened. This is well summarised in Horatio Bonar's hymn: 'Lord I confess to Thee sadly my sin; All I am tell I thee all I have been. Purge Thou my sin away, wash Thou my soul this day. Lord make me clean'. Heart opened.

There is another situation where the heart is to be truly opened to God and that is when the human heart is seriously, desperately in trouble. A particularly poignant example is the prayer (Psalm 88) of the musician Heman, a man greatly gifted as a singer and active in the praise of the Temple.[15] The background of this prayer is not known; here is trouble without explanation, he is 'full of troubles'. Perhaps it is just as well that we are unenlightened about the nature of Heman's predicament because then this prayer can become the cry of any troubled believer who is 'in the depths of the pit' of despair. A prayer then for all tortured and persecuted believers down through the ages.

This 'close to death' psalm commences in gloom and ends in even deeper gloom and darkness. Almost no let up. He is full of trouble. The saddest song of all from beginning to end. Indeed, the words he uses are almost unbearable to read. He speaks of being in the 'darkness of the deepest pit', of being 'shut up', 'cut off', 'cast adrift', 'afflicted', 'far from God', forgotten by God. He is 'in the land of forgetfulness'. It is almost as if he is already in the grave, one of the walking dead. In his loneliness he has no friend on earth or in heaven; 'lover and friend are far from him'. A complete catalogue of woes from beginning to end; almost unique in Scripture in its desolation. Yet Heman is being completely honest, he is telling God 'how it is'. His heart is raw, yet he is almost terrifyingly open, he pulls no punches, holds nothing back. He is being real. Yet in all these cries, screams even, from a deeply wounded emotional open heart, he is actively engaging with God. God is

---

13   2 Samuel 12:13.

14   Psalm 51:3.

15   1 Chronicles 6:33; 2 Chronicles 5:12.

his God and he still knows deep down that it is only in God, the 'God of his salvation' that help is to be found. He knows, deep down, that God's plan for him encompasses more than this single day; there is another page beyond the one that seems to have closed. That too is the lesson for us, whatever our situation, to be completely honest with God telling him 'how it is' with us, opening our wounded heart to him.

As the cardiac surgeon might say, 'open – to reveal the damaged heart'. And then – 'to work'.

P is for PROTECTION
(SALVAGE, SALVATION)

'This is not your own doing; it is the gift of God.'[1]

These words have a similar meaning. Thus 'protect' means to shield from harm or destruction, to guard from attack. 'Salvation' (coming from both Latin and Greek words meaning to deliver, rescue or preserve) can mean both to save or rescue from some dangerous or unfavourable situation when it has already occurred; or from some real threat of potential danger, warding off, protecting from, some impending disaster before it has happened. Both meanings are applicable to the heart and, in the spiritual sense, to an individual facing spiritual danger. First then we think about how these words apply to the physical beating pumping heart.

As we have seen, when blood flow to the heart muscle through the coronary arteries is drastically reduced then those muscle cells, supplied by the offending artery, begin to die. How long this takes depends upon the efficacy of any remaining blood flow. The question as to whether it is possible to prevent heart cells dying is one that has long intrigued both basic scientists and cardiologists. If it is possible then two questions follow. First, is it possible to prevent susceptible cells dying in the first place by interventions before the onset of the blood flow reduction has occurred. Second, is it possible to save, rescue or salvage cells, once the process of dying has already started, thereby reducing the area of damage. This latter is called 'infarct size limitation' and we will deal with this first.

The immediate problem once a coronary artery has become occluded, most commonly following the rupture of a lipid-rich atherosclerotic plaque, is to reopen the vessel and thus restore flow. This is called reperfusion. There are two possibilities. Firstly, as we have seen, since the occlusion is (usually) due to the accumulation of cells, and especially platelets at the occlusion site, we could attempt to 'dissolve' the clumps

1 Ephesians 2:8.

of these accumulated cells with anticoagulant, thrombolytic drugs such as, in earlier times, heparin or aspirin. Attempts at reperfusion could be performed under 'out of hospital' situations, such as in the ambulance before the hospital is reached. The argument for this approach is that the dying of cardiac cells is time dependent and the sooner flow is restored the better. The extent of myocardial salvage depends critically on how soon reperfusion can take place. Medical students are told 'time is muscle' and, by implication, 'time is life'. Speed saves. Drugs (pharmacological reperfusion or thrombolytic therapy) given orally or better, intravenously administered and given out of hospital, remains the most widely used method of restoring blood flow, particularly in developing countries and where the journey time to hospital is long. This is true even where catheterisation laboratories are available once the hospital is reached.

The other means of removing a blockage in a coronary artery in order to regain flow (called primary angioplasty or percutaneous coronary intervention, PCI) is to use a catheter placed inside the affected artery. This means inserting a fine, flexible, hollow tube – a process called catheterisation – into a suitable artery (usually in the groin or wrist) and advancing it into the coronary artery under X-ray or fluoroscopic control. These catheters usually have a balloon at the end which is then inflated to widen the artery. This does two things; it mechanically dislodges the offending material 'washing' some of it downstream; it also pushes some of it back into the inner wall of the artery.

Here follows a rather crude analogy! PCI is somewhat similar to a plumber clearing a blocked sink by 'prodding', pushing away the offending 'gunk' with a flexible stiff tube smaller in diameter than the draining tube itself. In a sink the problem is usually at the bend of the pipe; in the coronary artery the block is often at a 'bend' in that artery or sometimes where a smaller artery leaves the main one. However, whereas in the blocked sink the material is pushed down into tubes of ever-increasing diameter, in the blocked coronary artery the vessels downstream are smaller and of ever decreasing diameter. One can visualise that these smaller vessels could themselves become blocked by smaller pieces of material, thereby not allowing complete reflow. This problem can be alleviated by infusing, from the inserted catheter, a thrombolytic substance (there are several 'new' ones) that are quite similar in mechanism to aspirin, to 'dissolve' much of the offending material.

One problem arising out of this procedure of angioplasty in a narrowed or occluded vessel is that the damaged area in the inner part of the wall of the coronary artery could be made worse, perhaps by the 'squashing' of the fatty tissue of the atheroma into that already damaged vessel. To prevent any further occlusion of the artery (called restenosis) stents are inserted. Stents are small metal mesh tubes, usually made from a mixture of chromium, cobalt or platinum, situated in the balloon complex which, when inflated expands so that the stent becomes fixed inside the artery. When the balloon is deflated the catheter can then be withdrawn leaving the stent in place which then acts as a kind of scaffold to keep the artery open. Most stents are coated with drugs that reduce the risk of restenosis and to aid healing of the vessel wall. These are called 'drug-eluting stents', in comparison to bare-metal stents. Some stents are made of bio-absorbable material which, over time, become absorbed into the body allowing the artery to re-form naturally.

For years a vigorous debate raged as to which therapy was best. It now seems clear that the method of re-opening an occluded or narrowed coronary artery by angioplasty is preferred because it results in fewer deaths, and rates of reinfarction and stroke, than does pharmacological reperfusion. This is presumably because there is greater myocardial salvage; fewer cardiac cells die. This salvage is critically time-dependent; there is a time window for the restoration of blood flow and this is brief, perhaps only within two to three hours of the onset of symptoms. Since the average time for a patient to present is two hours then it is clear that speed is of the essence. It also means that before angioplasty can take place in hospital, thrombolytic drugs such as aspirin should be given as early as possible. Yet even if given within 30 minutes of the onset of symptoms it could take another 60 minutes or so for possible recanalization. This time window for salvage also depends on other factors such as the number of coronary collateral vessels, perhaps whether ischaemic preconditioning has occurred (see below) or if the demand of the heart for oxygen has been reduced. This is why quietness, light sedation and the assurance of medical personnel are important both on the way to hospital and when there.

So far, we have considered the situation where a coronary artery occlusion has already occurred and a myocardial infarction is in progress. But what about reducing damage to the heart before damage has occurred – protection rather than salvage? This leads us to the fascinating concept of preconditioning: the remarkable ability of the heart to defend itself against the damage that would result from a reduced coronary blood supply. Preconditioning is then a protective response resulting from brief episodes of a reduced blood supply or of increased myocardial oxygen demand. When this occurs, the heart is protected against a subsequent more pronounced damaging insult and this inherent protection lasts for some time (hours or even days). Originally the concept came from experimental studies involving purposeful but brief (a few minutes) coronary artery occlusions. These were found to reduce the degree of ischaemic damage that resulted from a longer permanent occlusion of the same coronary artery. Later it was found that this protection also results from rapid cardiac pacing, exercise and, particularly relevant to clinical situations, from the occlusion of an artery some distance away from the heart. This quite simple procedure is called 'remote' preconditioning. Here is an example: a certain amount of myocardial injury occurs during cardiac operations, for example during coronary artery bypass surgery. The extent of this injury can be measured by the release into the general circulation of enzymes which come specifically from injured cardiac tissue. The main enzyme is called troponin-T. 'Remote' ischaemic preconditioning can be induced before the operation quite simply by briefly inflating a cuff placed around the upper arm and then increasing the pressure inside the cuff to that well above normal (systolic) blood pressure. This is done for several short periods of a few minutes, deflating the cuff between inflations. Keeping the cuff inflated for longer periods could result in severe injury to the limb since inflating the cuff cuts off the blood supply to the arm rendering it ischaemic.

When this preconditioning procedure is performed prior to cardiac surgery the damage to the heart by the operation is reduced. We have given the ischaemic heart a 'shot in the arm'! Similar protection can be achieved by occluding other arteries, including those to the leg and, experimentally, to the kidneys and intestines. The mechanisms of this protection are unclear; the release of some endogenous protective substance from the ischaemic limb which would escape clearance by the lungs is one possibility or, more likely, some mechanism involving the sensory nerves arising from the occluded limb itself; in other words, a neural mechanism mediated via the brain. Whatever the mechanism, preconditioning shows that 'the body looks after itself', in this case the 'itself' is the heart. It results in salvage, or protection, a reduction in injury, by a mechanism outside, that is external to, the heart. In theory such a simple technique could be used to protect any organ from excessive injury during surgical interventions.

There is another possible intervention (called 'endogenous mammalian heart regeneration') which has aroused considerable recent interest and, indeed, has been described as 'a milestone in the history of cardiac cell therapy'. This attempts to repair the damaged, failing heart by injecting stem cells (called cardiac progenitor cells), which can 'heal' injured tissue. These are self-renewing cells derived from the bone marrow, or from the heart itself, which are robustly capable of differentiating into all three main cell types in the heart: cardiac muscle cells (called myocytes), vascular smooth muscle cells and the endothelial cells which 'line' the blood vessels. These stem cells, which are remnants of cardiac progenitor cells from the hearts of the developing foetus, are given into a coronary artery or by direct injection into, or placing over, the part of the heart surrounding the area of damage (called the 'peri-ischaemic zone'). Such direct application of such stem cells might be particularly effective. Certainly, this treatment strategy for cardiac regeneration after myocardial infarction could well have future potential.

The above examples are concerned with protection of the heart by a reduction in injury (the degree and extent of damage) by some external intervention. Now, 'protection' and 'salvation' are biblical words and both refer to something that happens because of an intervention external to an individual. In the above examples the physical heart does not save itself; the help has come from outside. This is precisely what happens in the spiritual realm to the inner, spiritual heart. The salvation is provided and comes as a free gift from a righteous God acting in love; it is 'not of or from yourself',[2] it is salvation by grace to the undeserving. There is only one way of salvation, one saving God and one saving work through which we are saved from the damaging, indeed fatal, effects of sin. It is open to all on the same terms. This is what Jesus came to do; he came as Saviour, as a bringer of salvation. This Saviour is 'Christ the Lord',[3] Christ is exalted 'as Saviour',[4] God 'brought' him as 'Saviour';[5] Jesus is both God and 'Saviour'.[6]

---

2 Ephesians 2:8.

3 Luke 2:11.

4 Acts 5:31.

5 Acts 13:23.

6 2 Peter 1:1.

God sent Jesus 'that the world might be saved through him'.[7] He is Saviour of the church[8] and indeed of all.[9] Specifically, this came through Jesus' death on the Cross; we are reconciled to God by the death of his son and we are saved by his life.[10] As we have seen for the physical heart, those wounded, damaged cells would die without external intervention, so it is with the spiritual heart. Without divine intervention, to rescue, to save, our inner heart would likewise die.

We would take it for granted that those dying material heart cells would want to be 'saved' because the consequences of not being rescued would be dire – without it even more damage would surely occur leading eventually to cardiac failure and the death of the whole organ. We could say that those damaged cells would want to be rescued for the sake of the whole organ. We might also conclude that just as damaged heart cells 'send out' a message by way of 'chemical indicators of need', so the spiritual heart would also communicate that it too needs help. By doing so it would be open to 'receive' a life-saving intervention. Could we also say that, just as for the damaged physical heart, the 'inner heart' would also be grateful for such help? For our spiritual salvation then we must admit our helplessness and accept the invited gift of God-provided salvation with contrite, thankful hearts. And, just as with the damaged, dying myocardium, it is impossible for the needs of the 'inner heart' to be fulfilled unaided; it requires external intervention. Even the necessary faith required to receive it is also a 'gift of God'.[11]

A simple illustration! Our daughter lives in the Northern Territories of Australia as a doctor in rural medicine. On our birthdays she sends a present, well wrapped, to our home address. We can see from the number and value of the stamps that this has been costly to send. And then there is the value of the present inside. There may also be a cost to receive the present if duty is payable at our end. Cost then both to send and to receive. There is the option to decline to receive the gift but of course we do accept it (and happily!) because we know who it came from. It was sent from someone who dearly loves us. We therefore receive the parcel, unwrap it

---

7   John 3:16; 4:42.
8   Ephesians 5:23.
9   1 Timothy 4:10.
10 Romans 5:10.
11 Ephesians 2:8.

and open. So it is with the offer of salvation from God. It comes from the Father's heart of love and is open to all. But, like receiving that present, we do have to personalise it, we do have to receive and accept.

We can also call this spiritual 'process' of receiving, regeneration or 'being born again',[12] just as we saw with the regeneration of the damaged heart following external intervention with stem cells. There is purpose in this intervention, we are not only 'saved by but saved for'. It is to enable us to 'walk in newness of life',[13] as Jesus himself walked, that is, lived[14] and ultimately, to become 'conformed to Christ',[15] to 'become like him'.[16]

Jesus wonderfully illustrated his teaching with stories. Most of which were parables although there were occasional references to real historical events; indeed, some of the parables were connected to such events. Illustrations are a good (and scriptural) way of getting a particular point across. We conclude this section then with real stories that illustrate (hopefully!) the spiritual truth about salvation.

Those young Thai footballers were discovered by two British divers for whom cave exploration was a hobby. To recover these boys from such an intricate cave system, most of it under water, was a formidable operation since each boy had to navigate very narrow passages and carry his own oxygen supply. Sometimes they were accompanied by an experience diver, sometimes they had to make the journey alone because of the narrowness of the underwater passages they had to pass. All the boys were rescued but one of the rescuers, a Thai marine Lieutenant-Commander Saman Gunan died in the attempt. 'Greater love has no man than this that a man lay down his life for his friends'.[17] He died trying to save others and there is now a memorial bronze statue to commemorate this action. As for the boys a year later they are 'doing well'. This is a picture, inadequate though it is, of the love of Jesus for the world dying for others, in their place. His death was substitutionary – 'in our place condemned he stood, sealed our pardon with his blood'.

---

12 John 3:3.

13 Romans 6:4.

14 1 John 2:6.

15 Romans 8:29.

16 1 John 3:2.

17 John 15:13.

The next story bears witness to the fact that Jesus came to earth to save in an obedient response to his Father's will. It is the true story, told on the radio many years ago, of the raising of an American submarine at the end of WW1. The young naval officer in charge of the operation was acutely aware that, while he stayed on the bridge in relative safety, his junior colleagues risked their lives below the surface of the sea. He decided to spend the winter period, when the operation was suspended because the weather was too dangerous to continue to salvage, training to dive so that he could take turn with those who 'went over the side', thus sharing their dangers below the sea. The illustration is this:

> Man, through his desertion of God, had got himself into a mess from which he could not rescue himself. When that happened, God wasn't content to give us good advice and direct the rescue operation from the bridge of heaven (or merely send his messengers to help us) but he himself came down from the bridge, and went over the side, without privilege or safeguard. And not only risked his life but gave his life for us.

The last of these three stories is more personal. When we lived in Nigeria, we managed to purchase, for our 'home leaves', a small bungalow in a village near to the beach town of Frinton-on-sea on the Essex coast. We became friendly with the secretary of the local church, one Norman Massie. Norman was captured by the Japanese in Burma and worked on the notorious Siam and Burma railway line, the subject of the film 'Bridge over the River Kwai'. Norman was one of the few survivors of this ordeal and, following the Allies advance, was taken back to Singapore and put on a boat to continue his internment in Japan. Norman wrote:

> After being deprived of writing materials for years it was ironic to discover that the ship's hold was loaded with pencils! In September 1944, in the China Sea, the submarines of our 'friendly' United States ally found us and torpedoed and sank the whole convoy. Those of us who survived were picked up from the sea and put into a cavernous whale factory ship to complete the journey to Japan. Off Formosa (now Taiwan) in very rough seas we heard a tremendous explosion which we assumed could only be another torpedo striking the ship and meaning another sinking from which we could not hope to again survive the treacherous waters. As a Christian for ten years and at that moment of extremity with death imminent, the words of a hymn flashed into my mind. It was about the glory of heaven! However, glory was deferred! The torpedo had been

meant for us but a Japanese escort destroyer had at that very moment zig-zagged and came in between and taken the blow. We were spared for another year of slavery in Japan. It gave me an unforgettable picture of our salvation – we all come under God's righteous judgement but the Lord Jesus has come between, taking the blow.

The one mediator.

What these stories illustrate is that salvation is not of ourselves, it comes (like myocardial salvage) from outside, from God himself. It results from the obedience of the Son Jesus to the Father's 'sending' and from his sacrificial death upon the Cross, taking our sins – that fatal damage to our spiritual hearts – on himself, bearing the brunt, taking the blow, in order that our spiritual hearts might live. This gift needs to be made our own.

Q is for the QUIET, PEACEFUL HEART

'Take heed, and be quiet; fear not neither be fainthearted'.[1]
'You will keep him in perfect peace'.[2]
'In quietness and in confidence shall be your strength'.[3]

'Let's have some peace and quiet' as my mother would often say to her boisterous sons. Certainly, peace and quiet are good for the heart as well as for the mind. For most of us this is when we are asleep, the 'heart at rest'. Sleep is of course a state of reduced awareness, not a complete cessation of activity. 'I slept but my heart was awake' said the author of the Song of Solomon (5:2). Just as well! So, in sleep (except in 'the sleep of death') the heart is still functioning but compared with the activities of daily living it is 'at peace' and is 'quiet'. This is because our bodies function in a pattern of distinct day and night cycles. At night, when the majority of us are asleep, our brains are being recharged and our hearts, whilst still maintaining the function of providing blood to the cells of the body, are beating more slowly, taking a rest. But certainly not stopping!

In one sense the physical heart is never 'at peace'. It never stops working, it is always 'on the go'; if it stopped you would stop too. However, there are times when the heart is less active, slower, less excitable and that is when we are asleep. It has long been known that, especially during NREM (non-rapid eye movement) sleep, the quiet, deep sleep from which it is difficult to be awakened and which makes up about 75% of a normal night of sleep, blood pressure and heart rate are much reduced. During dreaming, which occurs mainly during REM (rapid eye movement) sleep, during which brain activity is similar to when we are awake, both heart rate and blood pressure are increased. This is an oversimplification because during a normal night of sleep these two phases alternate such that sometimes

---

1   Isaiah 7:4.

2   Isaiah 26:3.

3   Isaiah 30:15.

there are up to five cycles, or clusters, of these two different sleep patterns, with accompanying changes in heart rate and blood pressure. Although studies are still ongoing, what we can be certain of is that heart rate during sleep can be less than 50 beats/minute and blood pressures as low as 20mmHg have been recorded. But, of course, the heart is still functioning and despite these changes in heart rate and blood pressure, cardiac output is largely maintained. And, the heart is not really quiet; one can still detect heart sounds, even more so than during the day because sleep usually occurs in a calm, peaceful and quiet environment.

What causes these changes in the activity of the heart during sleep? The slowing of the heart (called bradycardia) is due to the increased activity of the vagal nerves to the heart, mediated from the brain, whereas the increase in rate (tachycardia) during REM sleep is due to the enhanced activity of the sympathetic nervous system. These changes are sometimes dramatic and can be accompanied by abnormal cardiac rhythms. Heart rate changes during sleep are also related to the pattern of breathing; slower during expiration, faster during inspiration. This is called the Hering-Breuer (inflation and deflation) reflex which arises from receptors in the lungs and is mediated via the mid-brain.

There is an interesting relation between sleep patterns (especially sleep duration) and heart disease. Good sleep is the foundation for good cardiac health; the heart as well as the brain is sensitive to even slight changes in sleep pattern. Too little sleep, of less than five hours duration, can result in sleep deprivation during which there is an increased risk of cardiovascular disease, including heart attacks and stroke. This risk is doubled if this deprivation is continued for years, making it an additional risk factor to physical inactivity, obesity and smoking. Clinical studies in this field are notoriously difficult to evaluate because so many other factors are involved and more controlled studies need to be undertaken.

It now seems that even short periods of sleep deprivation (of one or two hours) has an immediate effect in increasing heart rate and arterial blood pressure; overdrive of the sympathetic nervous system is again the culprit. Even the loss of just one hour of sleep, as happens when the clocks are moved forward in March for daylight saving, has an effect; there is an observed increase in heart attacks the following day. Losing then even one hour's sleep is not trivial for the heart. The reverse happens when the clocks are moved back in the autumn. We can conclude then that unhealthy sleep results in an unhealthy heart. Some examples: in a Japanese study of 4,000 male workers, sleeping for less than six hours resulted in a five-fold increase in cardiac arrest compared to those workers who slept on average of more than six hours. In a different study, of men over the age of forty-five, those who slept for less than six hours were twice as likely to have a stroke or cardiac arrest than those who slept between seven and eight hours. However, sleeping more than nine hours a night also increases the risk of heart attacks and stroke. What then is the ideal? Seven is again the 'perfect number' for, as Macbeth put it, 'sleep knits up the balm of hurt minds'. And, we might add, of hurt, tired, unquiet hearts.

Seventeen-year old Randy Gardner, in breaking the world record for staying awake (he managed eleven days and twenty-five minutes before collapsing) discovered that his senses of taste, smell and hearing went haywire and that thereafter he suffered for years from bouts of insomnia. No records, as far as I know, were made of his heart condition but this rather foolish experiment did prove that 'sleep is essential for the health of the brain'. And, one might surely add, for the heart as well. It raises the general question of the effect of sleeplessness on cardiovascular health. Those mountains of anxiety, the dread of expectations placed upon us by others, as well as self-imposed, the distress of living at a frantic pace, when what we really need is 'a heart at peace', a tranquil sound heart, which gives life to the body, as the author of the book of Proverbs puts it.[4]

The words for peaceful, quiet, tranquil come often in Scripture. They mean more than the absence of war or of quarrels; more even than freedom from annoyance. Quietness is an underlying condition of serenity, a calm spirit, despite whatever bustle of activity there is around us. It is to be in command of oneself. It is an attitude based on confidence and trust. An Old Testament example: Psalm 131 speaks of having a 'quieted and still soul', like a child at its mother's breast, a heart 'quieted within me' despite what can be externally the very opposite.

Etty Hillesum in enemy occupied Amsterdam read daily in the book of Psalms and wrote of her experiences in her diaries. In May 1942 she wrote this: 'my own heartbeat is difficult to describe: so slow, so regular and so soft, almost unruffled but so constant as if it would never stop; neither war nor any other senseless human atrocity will ever be able to change it'.[5] Despite

---

4   Proverbs 14:30.
5   Patrick Woodhouse, *Life in the Psalms*, Bloomsbury Press, 2015.

the persecution, oppression, despotism and terrible sadism, Etty's heart was at rest. She was taken to Westerbork, a transit camp for Auschwitz, where she eventually perished in November 1943. What was the reason for this unruffled, 'soft' heart? Seemingly, her relationship with God, her prayer life 'an uninterrupted dialogue, eyes raised towards heaven with tears of emotion and gratitude'. Gratitude, and in such a situation. Etty's story is movingly retold in Patrick Woodhouse's book.[6]

To return to Psalm 131, a 'picture of contentment', 'permeated by the most perfect and sincere resignation' and once described by Charles Spurgeon as 'one of the shortest psalms to read but one of the longest to put into practice in our daily lives'. Those of us who have seen our children or grandchildren in the arms of their mothers, lying with unquestioning contentment, 'steadied and silent', in total relaxation and with the absence of fear or fretfulness, can sense the picture behind verse 2. Or as a 'weaned child' holding the hand of a trusted companion as they walk together.[7] Safe! It is a lovely and very contemporary picture of a childlike trust in God. Of the daily walk, with the Lord alongside in the heart, content that he is there. As Alec Motyer puts it, 'as a child who has gone beyond seeing its mother as a source of supply of nourishment'. It has entered the stage of simple contentment from just being where it is. It is a picture of a child weaned from being helpless to a position of childlike security. It suggests a discovered independence yet, at the same time, alongside a trusty dependence on a person who, in the past, has proved trustworthy. Contentment with confidence. This is so counter-cultural to the get ahead, pushy, improve-self society of today.

'I've cultivated a quiet heart'. Not completely still of course, the heart is still moving, nor quiet in the sense of absence of noise - for even at rest the physical heart is still a noisy organ. And, 'cultivated', the word Peterson uses in his paraphrase of this psalm, is absolutely right. Contentment, the 'quiet heart' does not come naturally, without effort; this spirit of contentment has to be learned.

The key it seems is understanding, living according to the priority of the health of our hearts as we hope in God.[8] 'Thou wilt keep him in perfect peace

---

6 Patrick Woodhouse, *Etty Hillesum, A Life Transformed*, Continuum, London, 2009.

7 Psalm 131:2.

8 Psalm 43:5.

whose heart (mind) is stayed on Thee'.[9] This comes through trust. As Paul put it much later:[10] 'I have learned (the key word) to be content in every situation, in need as in plenty', in the ups and downs of life. And, this Paul was able to say despite the situation in which he found himself. He was still a captive, in prison perhaps, bound between Roman soldiers, enclosed in a narrow cell, deprived of comfort and, perhaps most difficult of all, just waiting. The explanation for this contentment is this: 'I can do all things through Christ who strengthens me'.[11] A lesson learnt, a lesson that took time to learn, a gradual learning curve. He had now moved from learning to knowing. Contentment then, that quiet heart, comes through believing God is in control of our circumstances; and it becomes both a witness to others and a blessing to us.

This peace, this quiet heart at ease, this inward serenity, is nourished by God's word. It is a gift, a legacy, the last will and farewell greeting of Jesus himself and his most precious possession - 'I am giving you my peace' he said, 'I leave it with you'.[12] It is a free gift bequeathed in love. And, it is something Jesus really wants us to have. It is a defence against disquiet, a peace based on reconciliation with God the Father. Our hearts are not to be troubled, not to be afraid. It is peace in a struggling world, a peace, a quiet heart, that no life experience can take away. When Jesus spoke these words he was in the midst of a maelstrom, the very storm centre of the world. During this last week of his earthly life he knew he was facing the ordeal of the Cross. And yet, despite this, there was in him a special peace that is entirely his ('my peace') and which he wants others to have; 'in me you might have peace'.[13] A peace to counteract trouble and fear.

Two illustrations might help. Two artists were once invited by their patron to set on canvas the idea of peace. The first painted a quiet lake, still, unruffled, desolate. Not a living creature in sight. The other chose a tumbling waterfall with, across the face of it, the branches of a mountain ash. On it, and in the spray, a robin singing quietly. The first painting was the peace of stagnation and death, the peace of the grave. The other a living peace in the midst of a living world, like the peace that comes from an intelligent trust in the word of Jesus, in God's goodness and in the acceptance of his will.

---

9   Isaiah 26:3.
10 Philippians 4:12.
11 Philippians 4:13.
12 John 14:27.
13 John 16:33.

The other illustration of the kind of peace of which Jesus was speaking comes from a story of Robert L. Stevenson's grandfather. It is a story about the building of the Bell Rock Lighthouse in the midst of a violent storm. Would the mooring of the boat hold? A wee boy crept up from below to the deck, the storm as bad as ever. On the deck, lashed to his post, stood the watchman. And there was a smile on his face. A heart fixed, content, at peace, quiet amidst the surrounding tumult.

There is one other answer to the question 'what is a 'quiet heart'? and that is acceptance. Acceptance of ourselves, of things past, of things present and future. Ourselves first of all. There are things about who we are that cannot be changed. We simply have to accept those things.

My dear wife had wished to marry someone who was taller than her. I did not quite make that; when we married over sixty years ago we were the same height but, with age, as often happens, I have 'grown downwards' and am now considerably shorter than she is. As one of my grandchildren joked – 'Grandad, you seem shorter than when I last saw you. How long will it be before you disappear altogether?' Well, short of some kind of 'height transplant' I will continue to lose height. There is nothing I can do about it. I just have to accept it and so does my wife! For, as the Lord Jesus said[14] 'can you (meaning me!) add a cubit (or even a few inches) to your height (your stature) by worry', by 'taking thought', or by anything else?

The Greek word can also mean 'age' rather than 'stature' and this is just as true too of our 'ordained' age. Although of course, we may prolong life by having a healthy lifestyle and avoiding potentially dangerous habits. However, there are other things about ourselves and our situations that are not possible to change such as certain things about the ageing process itself. Despite what some would have us believe! The gradual wearing out of the body in which we presently live, anatomical (see above!) and physiological changes that are the natural consequence of 'growing old'.[15]

We may be able to delay some effects of ageing but, ultimately nature, as God decreed, has its (her?) way. They are inevitable. True, we have to accept them but we can also rejoice because, as God has promised, 'as your days so your strength will be'.

---

14 Matthew 6:27.

15 Jim Parratt, *Marvellously Made*, Handsel Press, 2017; Derek Prime, *A Good Old Age*, 10 Publishing, 2017.

Then, we have to accept the past. As we look back, and as we (hopefully) 'grow in grace', we can see more clearly the often dark path we have left behind us, the poor choices we have made, the things we have done for which we are now deeply ashamed, the accompanying sense of guilt, the people we have let down, the people we have hurt – including ourselves and especially God. But now, the past is past; there is nothing we can do about it. What is done really is done. Even God cannot 'unhappen' the things that have happened.

So, what can we say? We could say, as Peter said to Jesus, 'depart from me for I am a sinful man O Lord!' And yet, as believers, we can no longer say that. We must simply accept our inherent sinfulness. As the apostle John reminds us 'if we say we have not sinned we deceive ourselves and make God a liar; his word is not in us'.[16] As we are reminded, by the Holy Spirit, of the failures and sins of the past, of our present unquiet hearts, then we can bring them to the Lord. We can ask God for his gift of forgiveness, 'God be merciful to me a sinner, create in me a clean heart, renew in me a new spirit'. We can take God at his word: 'if we confess our sins God is faithful and just to forgive us our sins, and to cleanse us'.[17] By a sincere repentance we can be brought back into a right relationship with God and with those against whom we have sinned and, having done so, we can leave those forgiven sins behind, we can shelve them and move on; they are well past their 'sell by' date. 'Forgetting those things that are behind'.

When Paul at the end of his life, was perhaps tempted to bring back off the shelf, to drag back from the past, his own heinous sins he found he was able to forget.[18] The past forgiven and forgotten. When we do that with our own past, as we are tempted to pull the past back into the present, then that peace, that quietness of heart returns. The peace of forgiveness, the past dealt with. The peaceful, tranquil, quiet heart.

There is a hymn, again by Timothy Dudley-Smith, that catches the essence of 'quietness'. For many summers I took the church services on the beautiful island of Colonsay in the Inner Hebrides. As one looks out of the window of the church there is a line of 'quiet hills' and this hymn was chosen to sing on many occasions. It became known to us as the 'Colonsay Hymn'.

Here it is on the next page:

---

16 1 John 1:8-10.

17 1 John 1:9.

18 Philippians 3:13.

I LIFT MY EYES

I lift my eyes
to the quiet hills,
in the press of a busy day;
as green hills stand
in a dusty land,
so God is my strength and stay.

I lift my eyes
to the quiet hills,
to a calm that is mine to share;
secure and still
in the Father's will
and kept by the Father's care.

I lift my eyes
to the quiet hills,
with a prayer as I turn to sleep;
by day, by night,
through the dark and light
my Shepherd will guard His sheep.

I lift my eyes
to the quiet hills,
and my heart to the Father's throne;
in all my ways,
to the end of days
the Lord will preserve His own.

Timothy Dudley-Smith

R is for the RESISTANT, HARDENED HEART

'Nabal's heart died within him, and he became as a stone.'[1]

'Alienated from the life of God due.... to their hardness of heart.'[2]

Clinically there is a perplexing phenomenon described as 'stone heart' that has been, albeit rarely, observed during open-heart surgery. It is where the heart appears almost frozen and is due to an irreversible contracture, a kind of cardiac *rigor mortis*. This results from especially long periods of oxygen deprivation. It is also seen under certain experimental conditions where it is due to calcium overload. Something similar is seen post-mortem after excessive alcohol ingestion over long periods, a condition called 'alcoholic cardiomyopathy'. There are both chemical and structural changes in the contractile proteins which impair the ability of the heart to contract. This also results in dilatation of the heart and in disorders of cardiac rhythm. Excessive alcohol imbibing over a shorter period of time as in Nabal's case, results in a condition known as 'binge drinking'. These individuals show cardiac damage (necrosis) quite different to that resulting from an acute thrombosis; their coronary arteries appear quite normal.

The background of the story about Nabal (1 Samuel 25) is that David and his men had protected Nabal's extensive flocks of sheep and goats when they were far away from home territory. Some might call this a protection racket! Nabal refused to pay, not even cash in hand, and failed to provide normal hospitality, an accepted obligation at the time. He was clearly a hard man, self-centred (note the number of times – seven – the first-person singular comes in verse 11) he was arrogant ('who is this David?'), rude ('shall I take my bread, my water and give it to men who come from I know not where?'), hostile, churlish, ill-natured and, like many such people, cowardly and frightened. David was after all on his

---

1   1 Samuel 25:37.

2   Ephesians 4:18.

way to meet with him with four hundred armed men. This was a rich landowner's arrogant response to a ragged band of the dispossessed.

Maybe this hostile response was accentuated by the fact that the evening before he was in 'high spirits' and very, very drunk. This was then the morning after of the night before! There was also his response to the news that his beautiful wife Abigail had given a gift to David. At this he 'blew his top'; and, 'his heart died within him'.[3] Interesting, at least from a clinical point of view, is that it was about ten days later that Nabal eventually died ('the Lord struck Nabal and he died') and that 'his heart became as stone'. But how did he die? Was this a stroke leaving him paralysed or was it a heart attack, a heart already damaged as a result of his drinking. The passage suggests that his feasting (as though he were a king) was a frequent occurrence and that the amount of alcohol consumed was excessive ('he was very drunk'). It was in this enfeebled, drink-shattered state that Abigail's news resulted in terror and shock. Maybe this situation had happened before. 'Those that cannot remember the past are condemned to repeat it'.

One diagnosis, in the absence of a post-mortem, would be that Nabal suffered a massive coronary thrombosis resulting in severe cardiac damage and myocardial instability so that ten days later he died of heart failure or from a fatal ventricular dysrhythmia. A 'stone heart' indeed. Later, Shakespeare used a similar imagery when Othello, in his anger, tells Iago 'my heart is turned to stone; I strike it, and it hurts my hand'. Another stone heart indeed!

The clinical stone heart is resistant to intervention. Now Scripture has a similar word to 'stone' when it talks about the 'hardened' heart. For example, when the people of Zechariah's day refused to pay attention to God's word through him and 'stopped their ears' in order that they might not hear, we read[4] that they 'made their hearts diamond hard' lest they should hear God's voice. The word diamond can also be translated 'as flint' – which is a very hard variety of impure silica. The result of this disobedience was that judgement followed – exile of the people to a foreign land. Each of these active descriptions of the people's responses – stopped, turned, refused to listen[5] – emphasises that it was the fault of the people themselves that their 'hearts were hardened'.

---

3 1 Samuel 25:37, 38.

4 Zechariah 7:12.

5 Zechariah 7: 11.

This attitude to God's word spoken through his servants the prophets runs like a dark thread through the history of the people of God. Another example comes at the end of 2 Chronicles where a 'stone heart' was true of the young king Zedekiah; he 'stiffened his neck and hardened his heart' against turning to the Lord.[6] It is difficult to turn with a stiff neck! And, what was true of the king was also true of his priests and his people. Indeed, they scoffed at the prophets and despised their words. As with the surgical 'stone heart' there was 'no remedy'. This pattern is seen throughout Scripture. Jeremiah complained that the people had a 'stubborn and rebellious heart';[7] they had ears but did not hear. Indeed, even their faces and foreheads are described as 'hard', harder even than flint.

One other key passage is that of Pharaoh and his confrontation with Moses in the story of the plagues (Exodus 7 through to 11). This raises a philosophical problem, that is between the freedom of choice that Pharaoh had and the action of God in 'hardening' Pharaoh's heart, 'I will harden Pharaoh's heart; he will not listen to me'.[8] If it was God who hardened Pharaoh's heart, controlling his responses, then where was the Egyptian ruler's freedom to choose? Where was his free will? However, when we examine this question from the biblical narrative, we find a progression. Initially, in response to the first five plagues, we find that this was Pharaoh's free choice – he 'hardened his heart'.[9] He then became trapped in the obsession which had taken hold of him so that even advice from his own leaders[10] was rejected. Later, from the seventh plague onwards (the plagues of hail, locusts, darkness, death of the firstborn) Pharaoh's 'probation period' was at an end and we read that it was the Lord who hardened Pharaoh's heart.[11]

There is an important principle here. This relates to a particular choice becoming a habit; when the number of times that a particular choice is made leads to habit forming. This loss of freedom to choose becomes gradual until we reach the point of no return. Is it possible always to return from a series of bad choices? When we pass the point where we no longer have

6 2 Chronicles 36:11-16.
7 Jeremiah 7:24; 11:8 and compare Ezekiel 3:7-9.
8 Exodus 7:3, 4.
9 Exodus 7: 13, 22; 8:15.
10 Exodus 10:7.
11 Exodus 9:12; 10:1, 20, 27; 11:10.

the freedom to choose then we become a slave to that habit. As Jonathan Sacks has pointed out, 'Pharaoh is a tragic figure, like Lady Macbeth in Shakespeare's play, or Captain Ahab in Melville's Moby Dick, trapped in an obsession which may have had rational beginnings, right or wrong, but which has taken hold of him, bringing not only him but those around him to ruin'. Pharaoh may have been the most powerful ruler of the ancient world yet he could not rule or control himself. Pharaoh is everyman!

In the New Testament the most appropriate word for 'stone' is porosis, which is the noun used of the 'hardening' of the heart. However, in English this means something rather different; from it we get the word 'porous', a structure being permeable to liquids. However, the word can also mean 'irremovable bone formed when a structure unites, impenetrable, a hardness, like marble rather than bone'. The word is used to describe the man who cannot see a lesson designed to teach him.[12] He is insensitive, impervious, incapable of seeing, no impression is made on his heart.[13] Further, it is used of the attitude of the Jewish leaders after the miracles Jesus had performed, such as the healing of the man with the withered hand on the Sabbath.[14] Deaf to the appeal God was making to them; resistant, stubborn to the human need for love. When conscience is so long stifled that it has ceased to function, the heart like the clinical stone heart, becomes ossified. Hearts of stone can only be replaced; they are impenetrable to the incision of the surgeon's knife.

There is another use of the word 'stone' in the New Testament; the word is *lithos* where it is used metaphorically of Christ[15] and also of believers.[16] These stones are neither hardened nor ossified – they are living! And how about the 'stone' in the resurrection account? This was a stone as an obstacle to Jesus. The women thought that they would be unable to meet with the body of Jesus, because of the stone across the tomb. But it had been 'rolled away'. The stone in the heart needs to be 'rolled away' for us to meet with the risen Christ!

---

12 Mark 6:52; 8:17.
13 2 Corinthians 3:14; Ephesians 4:18.
14 Mark 3:1-5; John 12:40.
15 Romans 9:33; 1 Peter 2: 4, 6, 8.
16 1 Peter 2:5.

S is for HEART STOP

'When Ananias heard these words, he fell down
and breathed his last.'[1]

It sometimes happens that the heart stops suddenly and prematurely. Up to that time it has chugged along sometimes quickly, sometimes more slowly, but over all those years it has kept going wonderfully well with no stopping for a rest. Then suddenly, out of the blue, it stops. And, when this happens so will you unless something is done to restart it by someone who, trained in cardiopulmonary resuscitation (CPR – also sometimes described as 'call, push and rescue') happens to be close by. When the actor Richard Wilson, the Scottish 'star' of the TV comedy 'One Foot in the Grave', fell from the balcony of a café in Hampstead and suffered a life-threatening heart attack, fortunately for him a doctor passing by gave resuscitation and took him to hospital. He was told by his heart specialist, 'Richard, 80-year olds don't normally survive this. You survived because there was a doctor passing by and I was on duty'. Certainly, Richard really did have one foot in the grave!

This sudden cessation of the heartbeat, and therefore its function as a pump, is called, not surprisingly, sudden cardiac death (SCD) or cardiac arrest. What could cause this disastrous event? Several possibilities. For example, the shock of entering very cold water has long been known to precipitate cardiac arrest. The likely reason for this is an interaction between a sudden increase in sympathetic activity, triggering the 'fight and flight' response described earlier, tending to increase the heart rate, counteracted by an opposing response called the 'dive reflex' attempting to slow the heart rate. The confusion between these two protective reflexes we were all born with, leads to a disturbance in cardiac rhythm. These abnormal rhythms, either a marked cardiac slowing (bradycardia) or acceleration (tachycardia) could lead to ventricular fibrillation. Then, the heart ceases to function as a pump and there is loss of consciousness. This is certainly one cause of death due to drowning.

---

1   Acts 5:5.

A very unusual case of sudden cardiac death was reported in June 2017 when, in France near the city of Mulhouse, a popular French 33 year old fitness expert and travel writer called Rebecca Burger was killed when she was hit so violently on the chest by a faulty siphon on a high-pressure canister that she suffered a heart attack. 'Heart stop'. Apparently, several accidents had previously resulted as a result of using these canisters, including the loss of an eye. A sudden, unexpected violent blow to the chest of even a fit person can lead to 'heart stop'.

Another somewhat unusual instance of cardiac arrest was reported in 2007 by a group working in the Department of Cardiology in Utrecht. A previously healthy middle-aged woman was resuscitated out of hospital and brought into the emergency department. Among the resultant abundant biochemical data was a marked change in blood potassium. This was the result of the excessive chronic intake of liquorice; somewhere between 65 and 165g of liquorice confectionery daily. She had become addicted to liquorice. This resulted in an increase in blood pressure (hypertension) and disorders of cardiac rhythm, the result of liquorice toxicity. When presented with a box of 'liquorice all sorts' take care!

The above are admittedly somewhat rare occurrences of 'heart stop'. More common are those underlying, often undiagnosed heart conditions especially in young athletes which tragically sometimes lead to sudden death – the 'athletic heart syndrome'. A recent report from Paris told of three young footballers aged twelve to eighteen who died suddenly, either whilst playing or just after a match, not unusually in the shower room. Cold water? The most likely explanation was sudden cardiac arrest, death due to 'heart stop'.

Although athletes are regarded as among the healthiest people in society the sudden and unexpected death of such individuals although uncommon, has raised profound attention and publicity. In a study of 29 elite athletes (aged 13 to 30 years) who died suddenly during, or shortly after participating strenuously in a variety of sports, their hearts when examined post-mortem showed structural heart disease was present in 22 of these cases.

Matthew Gadsby played football for the Conference North side Hinkley United and collapsed during a 2006 league fixture against Harrogate. Three weeks later came the confirmation that he had died from 'arrhythmogenic right ventricular cardiomyopathy' (ARVC) a genetic condition which enlarges the heart due to muscle thickening. This went unnoticed until, as in Matthew's case, it resulted in sudden cardiac death. In 80% of people with the condition it is only found post-mortem, yet it can now be identified by simple screening. Matthew's tragedy came to the attention of CRY, a charity that raises awareness of cardiac risk in young people; one estimate is that at least twelve people aged 35 and under die each week from sudden cardiac failure of the kind that killed Matthew.

When in Australia a few years ago I watched the England cricket team humiliated by Australia. A wipe-out. One of the few positives for England was the performance of James Taylor, the small (in stature) fleet footed batsman from Nottinghamshire. In the February (2015) Melbourne one day/night match Taylor was 98 not out (from 90 balls and just two short of a maiden international century) when the last man Jimmy Anderson was run out (incorrectly, as it turned out due to an umpiring error). At the opening of the following season, in April 2016, Taylor turned up to play for his county at Fenners, the Cambridge University ground. However, during the warm-up he experienced tightness of the chest and his heart started to race. Taken to hospital he was diagnosed with ARVC and fitted with an internal defibrillator which would 'shock' his heart should it stop. His playing days were over. He is at present a British Heart Foundation ambassador. His comment on the situation was 'there is no scarier feeling than when your heart goes haywire; it's being on the edge of life with no control about whether you are going to plunge over the side'.

The most publicised case of SCD in an athlete was that of the Bolton footballer Fabrice Muamba. He suffered a cardiac arrest during in a FA Cup quarter-final against Tottenham Hotspur in 2012. He was technically dead for 78 minutes with folk trying to revive him using cardiopulmonary resuscitation. 'What would happen if somebody collapsed for ten minutes with no oxygen?' he said afterwards, 'the outcome would be very bad'. Something of an understatement! 'You would be brain-damaged. But 78 minutes? You think why. I tried to live my life as well as I could and when I was in trouble, he rescued me', speaking of the Chaplain of the club who helped save his life. That day the Reebok Stadium had become a kind of church with people praying for him on the pitch. Phil Mason, the only Chaplain employed full-time by a football club in the UK, later opened the stadium for fans and locals so that they could 'pop in' and say a prayer for the hospitalised footballer. 'People are praying for you', Muamba was told. 'That kind of news strengthens your faith. Maybe ten seconds of prayer helped me to get where I am today', Muamba said a year later. 'Prayer has been the word and long may that continue'. 'The fact that a collective unit of people are praying together is important in this journey,' said Owen Coyle. There is now a plaque which the Bolton players pass every time they go out onto the pitch, which says 'faith, family and football'. The newspaper heading read 'miracle man returned to life by his faith'. Healed by the strong combination of resuscitation and prayer.

However, the most common cause of 'heart stop' is not genetic, or even the result of using exploding canisters or liquorice over-dosage, but the sudden occlusion of an already narrowed coronary artery with subsequent ventricular fibrillation and cessation of the heart to perform as a pump. In the case of Richard Wilson, and Fabrice Muamba, there was someone on hand to provide cardiopulmonary resuscitation; sadly, for Matthew Gadsby and Rebecca Burger (and so many others) there was no-one on hand to help.

However, certainly in Scotland, the number of people successfully resuscitated by CPR following a cardiac arrest is on the rise. The latest statistics from the Scottish ambulance service show that 66% of patients suffering a witnessed cardiac arrest by paramedics were successfully resuscitated and alive on arrival at hospital. Specialist rapid response 'flying' ambulances to reach cardiac patients, and the training of firefighters in CPR techniques, were first used in Seattle in the USA as long ago as the 1960s, quickly followed by the Belfast Royal Victoria Hospital group of Pantridge and Adgey. The survival rates were quite dramatic. However, the urgent, life-threatening situation of 'heart stop' means that in most cases it is a family member, or a member of the public, who is first on the scene. This emphasises the importance of training individuals in cardiac resuscitation so that these 'community first-responders' can begin to administer CPR until such time as medical personnel arrive. Response speed is so important; for every minute that a patient doesn't receive CPR their chances of survival decreases by 10%. Scotland's unique 'National Strategy to Improve Out of Hospital Cardiac Arrest' survival rates through a 'Save a Life Scotland' campaign, plans to train 50,000 people in CPR together with 1,000 public access defibrillators in suitable places. These approaches, long delayed, could save around 1000 lives in Scotland by 2020.

There are few examples of what might have been sudden cardiac death in Scripture: and, not surprisingly, no post-mortem evidence. Let us look at them. The first comes in the Old Testament (1 Samuel 25) and concerns a rich farmer called Nabal. The story was told earlier in the previous chapter.

Nabal was rich indeed with three thousand sheep and one thousand goats, a home near Carmel and a wife called Abigail who was both beautiful and intelligent. David was then a fugitive fleeing from King Saul and he and his men had met up with Nabal's shepherds and had protected them from marauding raiders. What concerns us here is the end of the story – and the end of Nabal, which is summarised in the phrase 'the Lord struck Nabal and he died'.[2] Certainly, the underlying problem was alcohol binge drinking, but on top of this was his tendency, also alcohol fuelled, to be angry, uncooperative and combative. We are told two things about his heart.[3] First, when Nabal heard, for him, the bad news about David's threat of retribution we read that 'his heart died within him' and that he became 'as stone'. We can take this phrase in two ways: either it was his heart that was turned to stone, a possibility discussed in the previous section, or that he himself became as stone. In other words, he became non-responsive, perhaps due to loss of consciousness, common in people dying suddenly because of the cessation of cerebral blood flow.

There is perhaps another Old Testament example.[4] The evil Pelatiah the son of Benaiah was a prince of the people who 'devised iniquity', gave 'wicked council' and prophesied falsely. He died suddenly in the middle of a true prophecy spoken by Ezekiel, declaring judgement. As Peter Craigie suggested, he died 'as though from a massive heart attack'. Perhaps sudden cardiac death following the shock of hearing a word of judgement against him?

Another example of someone dying suddenly comes from the New Testament and concerns the death of a church 'member' called Ananias.[5] His death was probably from a cardiac cause heralded by an abrupt loss of consciousness (absence of cerebral blood flow) within a short time of the onset of acute symptoms. Heart stop. 'When Ananias heard the words (of Peter) he fell down and breathed his last'. Was this the result of a sudden dramatic increase in heart rate leading to ventricular fibrillation? The story behind this death was one of shame and the agony of detection felt by Ananias, 'the horror of a conscience not yet dead', because of his hypocrisy, dishonesty and avarice, and that of his wife Sapphira. The two had sold some property and kept back part of the proceeds for themselves (quite

---

2   1 Samuel 25:38.

3   1 Samuel 25:37.

4   Ezekiel 11:13.

5   Acts 5:1-10.

legitimate) yet, in presenting the rest to the young church they had given the impression that all of the proceeds had been given. Hence, Peter's words 'you have lied to God', you are 'testing the Spirit of the Lord'. When Sapphira appeared on the scene, not knowing her husband had died, she too lied and, when told of her husband's surmise, she too 'fell down and breathed her last'; dead and with no opportunity to repent. The sudden terrible news resulted in shock and 'heart stop'. No wonder then that at this, 'great fear came among the whole church'. It is a truly terrible thing to fall into the hands of the living God.

Of course, 'heart stop' comes to all; it is inevitable. Yet any death is deeply personal. It is the 'final journey of the soul' and for some 'slipping into a cortex unknown'. If we had a choice (we don't!) I suppose a death that is sudden has much to commend it. Two of my friends recently died this way, one when watching a film in a cinema. For some there is the terror of leaving this world,[6] the 'cords of death'.[7] Even Moses was afraid of death.[8] We live 'in the shadow of death'.[9] For some there may the regret of leaving a loved-one behind, or of so much left undone, the sorrow of not seeing future generations growing up. Yet, there is a positive way to die. We 'come from God', and we are 'going to God'. Life is a pilgrimage to God; it is no aimless wandering. We live in the certainty that God is with us, wherever we go and whatever happens. And, this includes dying. Jesus said 'those who believe in me have eternal life'; he goes to prepare a place for us. It is a place with him in his Father's house.[10] We 'come to the Father' through him. It is 'by the blood of the Lamb', through his redemptive work on the Cross of Calvary, that we find our home (and what a home!) with him in heaven. And, in the process of the 'going' we are accompanied by the one who never leaves us nor forsakes us'.[11]

It seems to me that Timothy Dudley-Smith is 'on the ball' when he writes 'I know who you are: you are my Saviour Jesus. I found you long ago: or rather you found me. Beckon me on, then Jesus my Lord and I will follow'.

---

6 Psalm 55:4.

7 2 Samuel 22:5, 6; Psalm 18:4.

8 Exodus 2:14.

9 Psalm 23:4; Matthew 4:16.

10 John 14:2, 3; Luke 23:42, 43.

11 Psalm 23:4.

T is for the TRANSPLANTED HEART

'I will give you a new heart.'[1]

'I will give them a heart to know me.'[2]

Organ transplantation (liver, lung, kidney and heart) are now common, albeit still technically demanding, surgical procedures and at present organ demand still greatly exceeds supply. Do carry an organ transplant card! The history of surgical transplantation is a long and exciting one with many experimental attempts, dating back over a hundred years or so, to replace an organ of a recipient with one from a donor. These were largely successful and paved the way for human organ transplantation.

The story of the first human cardiac transplant operation in 1967 is well known and was then as momentous medically as the moon landing made shortly afterwards. However, what is not so well known was that similar operations had apparently been performed years earlier (in 1940 and 1946) by a remarkable Soviet investigator Vladimir Demikhov. It was only much later (in 1960) when a book of his experiences was translated into English that these studies became more widely known. The present author also has a personal recollection of scientific work only appreciated when translated from Russian into English. It was in the early 1960's that I discovered a book on coronary blood flow regulation by the Russian pharmacologist Natalia Kaverina. This became a stimulus for some of my own work and later during a visit to Moscow I was able to meet Dr Kaverina. How much, I wondered, in the history of science, is 'hidden' because it was originally published in languages (perhaps Japanese, Russian, Arabic, Chinese) which, at least at that time, were not understood and read by scientists in the West.

It was only in 1967 that Dr Christiaan Barnard, described as 'a dashing young South African surgeon' attempted what is now acknowledged to be the first human heart transplant. He was in receipt of a heart of a twenty-six year-old non-Jewish woman (Denise Darvall) who had been fatally

---

1   Ezekiel 36:26.

2   Jeremiah 24:7.

injured by a car whilst crossing a road. Barnard removed the diseased heart from Louis Washkansky, a fifty-four-year-old male Jew, and this was then replaced with the woman's living heart. The 'heart swap' man thus received a heart that, to the excitement of the surgical team and indeed of millions world-wide, commenced to beat and continued to do so for eighteen days.

There were questions for Mr Washkansky. 'How does it feel, as a man, to have a female heart?' and 'as a Jew, how does it feel to have the heart of a non-Jew?' The operation apparently also worried Mrs Washkansky; she was concerned that her husband would no longer love her because she believed that the heart, as a symbol of affection, controlled both personality and emotions. 'I thought the heart controlled all your emotions and personality,' she said. Is the ultimate symbol of human affection reduced to a clinical convenience? Indeed, there are some fascinating experiences, not easy to verify, of recipients of donor hearts seeming to take on some of the personal characteristics of the demised donor. This raises the question of the relation between heart and mind. After all, the heart does have its own neural 'control centres', the mind within the heart.

The next heart transplant Barnard performed was more successful but even more controversial in apartheid, racist South Africa. This was because a coloured man (Clive Haupt) was the donor and a white man (Philip Blaiberg) the recipient. Blaiberg survived for nineteen months. In such a society the operation stimulated discussions, often heated, about whether a white man with a coloured man's heart should still be able to go places from where 'coloured people' were generally excluded. As one newspaper editor wrote 'there is no provision in the Group Areas Act for black hearts to beat in white neighbourhoods'. So, Mr Haupt was guilty of infringing the law. Posthumously.

Much of the controversy about cardiac transplantation arose because of the place the heart has with our cultural links and notions of personal identity. The functional symbolism of the heart deep rooted within us raises troubling ethical, legal (and financial) implications.

One fundamental question was whether the heart is merely a mechanical pump so that the operation becomes 'quite a simple plumbing job', as one pioneer surgeon described it, or is there more to it than that? Is the heart more than a pump? As Pascal wrote 'the heart has its reasons, which reason does not know'. A heart that reasons? Does the heart have mind of its own, its own 'intelligence', that can make decisions? Is there a kind of cardiac cellular memory? Can aspects of personality really be 'transferred' from person to person during transplant operations (there are apparently some rather surprising examples of this) or is it simply that the recipient simply imagines things about the donor – especially if the organ transplanted is the heart? What we do know is that the heart has neurons with connections to, as well as from, the brain and has 'messengers' such as neuropeptides that could encapsulate memories. Is the ability of the heart to 'remember' a preconditioning stimulus (see the chapter on P for protection) one such example? Many questions, most unanswered, about the relationship between mind (brain) and heart.

Another question relates to the heart and death, whether a person is only 'dead' when the heart stops. This discussion led to a fundamental re-evaluation and redefinition of death as 'the loss of meaningful brain activity', rather than cessation of the heart beating. There are further legal implications here. A law, introduced in Parliament as a Private Members Bill by Geoffrey Robinson MP, was passed this year (2019) to allow organ transplantation without consent. This law is named after two children, a six year-old girl called Keira Ball from Devon killed in a car crash, who 'gave' her heart to a nine year-old boy, Max Johnson, who was then in the Freeman Hospital in Newcastle with heart failure following a viral infection and who was not expected to live. 'I was ready to die – I didn't think I would make it', he said. In all, Keira's organs were used to save four lives. It was moving to see both sets of parents around Max's hospital bed during his recovery from the operation. The law, which gives presumed consent for organ donation, is now known as 'Max and Keira's Law'.

Incidentally, such heart transplant operations are only possible because of the invention a decade earlier, of the heart-lung machine which 'takes over' the blood circulation during the period of surgery. The origin of this machine goes back much earlier, to the work of surgeon Michael DeBakey, the child of Lebanese immigrants to the USA, who as a medical student at Tulane University in New Orleans in the 1930's, built a 'roller pump' which would later become part of the heart-lung machine.

The early attempts at heart transplant operations were followed by years of failure. Indeed, the American Heart Book, published in 1980, has little to say about heart transplantation, since they 'involve a degree of surgical skill that is within the capability of a very few specialists'. What was it then that reversed the years of failure to the present-day situation where over

3,000 heart (and heart and lung) transplants are performed annually? A number of things: improvements in the design of 'heart blood' machines and in surgical skills, better methods of cardiac protection before the transplantation and the development of better anticoagulants to prevent blood clotting. Especially important was the use of 'perfusion hypothermia' for keeping the donor heart cold. This was pioneered in the late 1940's by Wilfred Bigelow and his colleagues in Toronto, Canada. Reducing the temperature of the donor heart decreases cardiac metabolism and hence oxygen requirements. This allows time, always an important factor, for the donor heart to be transported.

This is particularly important because the viability of donor hearts deteriorates rapidly where the transport distances are vast. In Australia for example, in 2015, of the 381 donor hearts available only 81 transplants were able to be performed because of the deteriorating condition of the donor heart on arrival. This was significantly improved (by up to 40%) through the use of a transportable device which 'feeds' the donor heart perfusing it with a cold, balanced and oxygenated solution of minerals and nutrients. This process (called *ex vivo* perfusion) enables donor hearts to be kept in better condition outside the body, reducing the extent of deterioration. It also allows organs to be sourced from wider afield, widening the donor pool. Certainly much better than the old ice box!

However, the main problem was the failure of the transplanted heart to 'take' within the recipient's body. As Peter Medawar showed in 1944 this rejection was due to an immunological reaction. This is the body fighting the new organ identified as a 'non-self'. Such rejection of donor organs stopped for many years heart transplantation surgery until the development of immunosuppressant drugs. This story is also of interest. It started with the 1988 Nobel Prize for Medicine won by the American biochemist Gertrude Elion. Her main interest was in the constituent parts of DNA, small molecules called purines and pyrimidines. Elion wondered whether these might be used as anti-leukaemia drugs and indeed one them, 6-MP was effective. It was suggested that this drug might also suppress the immune system and the British transplant surgeon Roy Calne used a related compound (azathioprine) to successfully suppress the immune system. Later this was replaced by the more active cyclosporine.

Gertrude Elion actually funded her PhD (never completed) by doing several poorly paid jobs to finance her studies at night school. No government funding in those far off days during WW2! And, it was only because many men working in the pharmaceutical industry were fighting in the Second World War that women began to be employed in their place; Elion only began to work as a senior research chemist a year before the war ended.

We now know that the key to preventing rejection probably lies in T-cells. These immune cells travel to the heart causing inflammation, one of the initial steps in the rejection process; if one can interfere with this migration then rejection of transplanted hearts could be prevented thus avoiding the severe side effects associated with existing treatments.

Many heart transplant surgeons have never lost a sense of wonder at seeing the lifeless, cold, yellow white, motionless, flaccid, empty donor heart, doing nothing and yet when 'plugged' into its new home in the recipient's body cavity, slowly turning pink as blood flow is restored and then the heart beginning to beat, pumping away quietly all by itself, without any outside help at all. 'Fantastic, you never get used to it. One of the most astonishing sights in medicine!' One of the great glories of science!

In Scripture, as we have seen, the word 'heart' has two distinct meanings. It can sometimes refer to that beating organ in our thoracic cavity without which life is impossible, but in the main the word heart refers to the 'hidden man', the 'real you', the governing centre which makes a person who they are. The 'essential me'. Such a heart is described as diseased, damaged, hardened, even uncircumcised! This is the kind of heart we all have. It means that with such hearts we are singularly unsuccessful in revealing God's character and nature to the world. Such a heart needs drastic surgery. Indeed, the only remedy is a new heart, simply tinkering with the 'old heart' is insufficient. It is too far gone. It needs to be replaced by a new one, responsive to God and to his word. The question is, 'how can this happen'?

This is the basis behind a wonderful passage in the Old Testament book of Ezekiel where God says 'I will give you a new heart and a new spirit I will put within you. And I will remove the heart of stone from your flesh and give you a heart of flesh'.[3] This was a promise to God's people in exile and captivity in Babylon. It was a promise of hope and reassurance. They were to be gathered and 'assembled' out of the countries where they had been scattered and would return to the land from which they had been taken, a land given to them by God. This then was a prophecy for a certain chosen people Israel and given for a certain time. Nevertheless, it has profound

---

3 Ezekiel 36:24–27.

implications for today's world; God's word is a living, active word'.[4] To be a Christian is to have received from God a new heart and a new spirit. It requires quite radical spiritual surgery. An inner transformation takes place which enables those who undergo this 'surgery' to live lives to the full and to the glory of God, to enable them to 'walk even as Jesus walked'[5] and to reveal to the world God's nature.

What does this radical spiritual surgery involve? First, as with cardiac transplantation, we have to accept that a such a new heart is needed and that no attempt at reformation, however sincere, would improve the situation. The tragic legacy of repeated past failures needs to be dealt with. It requires the old, cold, lifeless heart of stone to be removed. It has to be excised. The 'cardiologist's' advice, on the basis of diagnosis, is that the present heart just will not do. It is quite unable to fulfil the function for which it was intended.

Second, this new heart is God given; 'I will give, I will put, I will cause'.[6] Such a new heart has to be available, there has to be a 'donor'. There is! The 'donor' is God himself. And, it has to be asked for, just as someone who requires a new physical heart has to agree to be put on the transplant list. And, we cannot do the operation ourselves; it needs an intervention. It needs the grace of God.

Third, provision has to be made for this radical heart surgery to take place. Preparations are required, just as in case of physical cardiac surgery. Just think of all that has to happen prior to the actual transplant operation. Many would say that in the spiritual sphere this is prayer, by one's self and by others on our behalf. Folk who have had such a spiritual experience would testify to the vital place prayer by family and friends have played in this process. Often there is a long build up before such a transformation can take place. It is often said that Paul's conversion on the Damascus Road[7] and part of his later testimony[8] was sudden, out of the blue. In fact, his hard, resistant heart had been softened by the Holy Spirit long before; there was heart preparation before his dramatic conversion.[9]

---

4 Hebrews 4:12.

5 1 John 2:6.

6 Ezekiel 36: 26,27.

7 Acts 9: 1-9.

8 Acts 22:1–11; 26:12-19.

9 Acts 7:58, 59.

Patients undergoing cardiac surgery of any kind need careful monitoring and care after the event. This is vital. It is also true of spiritual heart surgery. The Lord had already prepared Ananias to care for Paul in the crucial days after conversion.[10] My own experience bears this out. The first time I heard the gospel was at a University Mission in November 1953 taken by John Stott. The 'follow up' was in the form of a class preparation for church membership, 'confirmation' (I attended All Souls Anglican Church in London). There were set patterns of Bible reading and participation in church and SU beach missions. But, as with Paul, and as with all cardiac operations, there was preparation before what took place before that mission. Unknown to me! These included being aware of a next-door neighbour going to church each Sunday morning (I went just once with him), enthusiastic Christians at school including the showing of a Fact and Faith film there, and a small but vibrant Christian Union at the College of the University I attended. 'Pre-evangelism' indeed. And, I must add, falling in love with one of my classmates and playing football with another believer – folk who revealed Jesus to me. So, as in cardiac transplantation, there is preparation, then the surgery and then good 'follow up'!

It seems to me that the passage in Ezekiel and the need of a new heart fits well with the command, and it is that, to be 'born again' of God's Spirit. As in Jesus' conversation with Nicodemus. 'You must', said Jesus.[11] It is a categorical imperative.

---

10 Acts 9: 10–19.
11 John 3:7.

U IS FOR THE UPSET, FEARFUL, TROUBLED HEART

'Let not your hearts be troubled neither let them be afraid.'[1]

The first, and subsequent signs of chest pain are especially frightening. Is it my heart or my stomach? Frightening, because you know you have only one heart and that your life is dependent on that one heart. We think here about the two most likely clinical situations that cause such pain and 'upset' and then about the spiritual situations to which they speak. 'Suddenly it felt as though someone had picked up a sledgehammer and whacked me in my chest. It was difficult to breathe, I was feeling sick and the pain, especially from my left shoulder, was now extending down both my arms.' (Incidentally this is because the sensory pathways from these areas run to the brain in the same nerve trunk as those from the heart.) 'I sat down but the pain continued'. Or this – 'I was walking uphill against a cold east wind and carrying two bags of heavy shopping when I experienced pain in my chest. When I stopped for breath the pain disappeared'.

In both these experiences the common symptom was pain but, apart from that, there are differences, although it is true that it is sometimes not easy to distinguish between the first and the second of these two scenarios. The first is 'typical' of a heart attack, the second of angina. What is the difference between the two? A heart attack (a myocardial infarction or coronary thrombosis) is when a coronary artery is so narrow that it becomes blocked. The characteristics are, as outlined in the case described above, severe pain in the chest, collarbone and neck which is so severe that one sufferer truly described it as being 'racked' with pain. This is pain that lasts a long time and is often accompanied by cold, clammy sweating and a feeling of nausea, sickness. It is interesting that women who suffer a heart attack often do not have central chest pain radiating down the left arm, but are more likely to experience symptoms like nausea, vomiting and shortness of breath. In one study almost half of women who had a heart attack had no

---

1   John 14:27.

chest pain at all. This sometimes makes diagnosis difficult; indeed, in one British Heart Foundation supported study from the University of Leeds, women with a total blockage of a major coronary artery were 59% more likely to be misdiagnosed then men. They also had a significantly greater risk of death.

The second example above was of *angina pectoris*. The word angina is derived from the Greek word *anchein* meaning 'to choke' and was first used by William Heberden in 1768. So now a little medical history! Heberden's description of the condition is remarkable: 'There is a disorder of the breast with strong and peculiar symptoms, considerable for the kind of danger belonging to it, and not extremely rare. The seat of it and sense of strangling anxiety with which it is attended make it not improper to be called angina pectoris'. His description continued 'those afflicted with it, most commonly in winter, are seized, while they walk soon after eating, with a painful and most disagreeable sensation in the breast which seems as if it would take their life away if it were to increase or to continue: the moment they stand still, all uneasiness vanishes'. Difficult to add to this description made as long ago as 1772! Yet Heberden himself did not know that the pain originated from the heart.

The link between the symptoms of angina and the state of the coronary arteries was made by Jenner, the discoverer of vaccination; indeed, it is to Jenner that credit should be given for first associating angina with the heart. The story goes that he was performing a post-mortem on a patient who had had anginal symptoms in life, when he found the knife grated as he cut through a coronary artery; he looked at the ceiling thinking that falling plaster was the cause of the sensation before he realised that the cause was in the artery itself. Later it was Burns in 1809 who made clear the association; 'when the coronary arteries are ossified or cartilaginous then every agent capable of increasing the reaction of the heart, such as exercise, compassion and ardent spirits, must be a source of danger'. A long-ago link of the heart, and the coronary arteries, with 'compassion', with love.

The pain of angina, and of a full-blown heart attack, is because of the presence within cardiac muscle of specialised pain receptors; nature keeps us from ignoring these feelings of unease when they are stimulated. Of course, this is one of the body's protective mechanisms against danger. Pain is, as the surgeon Paul Brand has it from his extensive studies on leprosy patients who had lost the ability to feel pain, the 'gift nobody wants'. It is not a blemish in creation, God's one great mistake, it is the gift 'nobody wants'. A sign, that 'something is not quite right'. Brand believed that although the existence of pain 'is the most problematic aspect of creation it is not antithetical to life but a requisite for it', part of God's survival strategy for the body. All pain is in the head; there it originates and there it dwells.

The pain of a heart attack, or of angina, is called 'ischaemic pain' and is due to a marked reduction of blood flow to the affected area concerned; or, more accurately, to the resultant pain-producing substances arising from cellular metabolism, that are not washed away. The latter is easy to demonstrate at home (without the heart being involved!). Simply tie a ligature tight around the upper arm to occlude the blood supply and then exercise the fingers or clench the fist repeatedly. The result? Pain. But, do not leave the ligature on for too long. No one-arm readers please! In fact, although pain receptors, and their relevant sensory fibres, are relatively few in the heart they 'recruit' pain receptors and fibres from other areas (arms, neck, jaw for example) as if they too were in danger, setting the alarm bells in the brain ringing. This 'referred' pain acts as a 'favour' to the heart, telling the brain that something is amiss and making sure it got the message about something 'not quite right'. They are 'borrowed' to draw attention to the real problem, which is in the heart.

Now for a summary of the key differences between a heart attack and angina. First, in angina the problem is a narrowing of the coronary vessels supplying blood to the heart such that, when the oxygen demands of the heart increase, as in exercise, too little blood can get through. This leads to the typical symptoms of chest pain and tightness. It is the old problem of the balance between supply and demand – in this case for oxygen. The pain is relieved by stopping the exercise; the symptoms go away after a few minutes rest, or by taking drugs called nitrates, usually in the form of a spray or as a tablet placed under the tongue. This is the simplest and most effective route of administration because blood flow to the buccal cavity allows rapid access of the drug to the general circulation and to the heart; absorption from the gastrointestinal tract is much slower. Although nitrates do dilate healthy coronary vessels it is unlikely that this is the predominant mechanism of their effectiveness. Most likely their main effect is to dilate the systemic veins so allowing pooling of blood in the periphery and a subsequent reduction of filling pressures in the heart. This is called 'unloading'.

Diversion! The story of nitrates and angina is an interesting one. Heberden had little to offer by way of treatment but this was changed by the discovery in 1867 by Thomas Lauder Brunton of the effect of inhaling amyl nitrite, an observation he made as a young resident doctor at the Royal Infirmary in Edinburgh. He was just 23. He had found that during an anginal attack the patient's pulse was smaller and the arterial pressure greater. He also observed that there was temporary relief of the pain following bleeding from a vein of 3 to 4 ounces of blood. He knew amyl nitrite also reduced blood pressure and thought it might benefit, much as bleeding had done. He described his great moment: 'On pouring 5 to 10 drops of the nitrite on a cloth and giving it to a patient to inhale . . . there was simultaneously flushing of the face and the pain completely disappeared and did not return'. He also used glyceryl trinitrate on himself but it gave him a severe headache (today still a side effect) and made him vomit so he considered it should not be given to patients.

Just a few years later at the Westminster Hospital in London William Murrell tried the remedy on patients and soon established its usefulness; over 150 years later it is still a 'drug of choice'. This story reminds us that many of the great discoveries in medicine, indeed in science generally, have been accidental, finding valuable things in unexpected places – serendipity. Or, as one perceptive Nigerian tribesman observed, 'scientists are like a chicken scratching around in the sand until it finds something'!

The second key difference between angina and 'heart attack' is that the pain in angina usually goes on resting, it is transient. In contrast, the pain following a heart attack is severe, long lasting, does not decrease on resting; furthermore, there is a danger of cardiac arrest, 'heart stop'. Call 999 immediately or send someone to do so if say, the pain has not gone away after resting for 5 minutes.

The physical heart under these conditions can be said to be 'troubled', 'upset' 'fearful', 'pounding' as we gulp for breath. And, of course, there are so many other situations in life that arouse in us a sense of fear, that emotional response to something unpleasant or, as in the case of heart pain, outright dangerous. Fear of the unknown, the unusual, the unexpected, fear of physical danger or of a forthcoming surgical operation, a fear of people (hurting people hurt other hurting people), fears about health (especially mental health), of poverty, death, loss, loneliness even fear of oneself. Unwanted life events that are truly upsetting. It is hardly surprising therefore that these three words (upset, fearful, troubled) come often in Scripture; they are characteristic of life in general. We live in a world in which terrible things happen.

Firstly, fear of the unknown, the unexpected, fear related to perplexity, to confusion, the inexplicable. When, for example, the disciples came to the tomb early on that first Easter morning they were afraid; 'their hearts were fearful'[2]. They were afraid of the dark, of the place of the dead and buried – a place where evil spirits abounded, a haunted place – afraid of the strange 'young man' at the tomb, afraid of such an unexpected meeting in such a dark, dismal place. Then they had trespassed into a private garden and were troubled about the stone rolled across the place where the body of Jesus had been placed. 'Who will roll away the stone?'[3] And, their hearts were not only afraid in such a dark place but also 'dark', because in their thoughts Jesus was dead; no one had ever survived crucifixion. Hearts 'dark', deeply upset, troubled, astonished, perplexed, 'we do not know where he is'[4] and, above all, afraid. No need to be! The word of the angel of the Lord and of Jesus himself – 'Do not be afraid'.[5] Certainly, they were still confused, there were things they still did not understand, but fear? No. The risen Christ was with them.

Then there is the fear of people. Here are some examples from the Old Testament. Jacob was afraid of Laban and of Esau, Joseph's brothers were afraid of him after the death of Jacob, Samuel was afraid of Eli, Saul was afraid of David and David of Saul, Ishbosheth the son of Saul was afraid of Abner and Jael was afraid of Sisera – no wonder! Elijah was afraid of Jezebel. This fear of people continues into the New Testament. Herod feared John,[6] the parents of the man born blind were afraid of the Jewish authorities,[7] as were Joseph of Arimathea[8] and the disciples after the resurrection, despite those locked doors.[9] So much fear! Hearts upset. Yet as Isaiah said 'who are

---

2 Luke 24:5.

3 Mark 16:3.

4 Luke 24:3, 4.

5 Matthew 28:5, 10 and compare Mark 6:50.

6 Mark 6:20.

7 John 9:22.

8 John 19:38.

9 John 20:19.

you to be afraid of mortal man, of man who dies'.[10] 'The fear of man is a snare'.[11] God has not given us a 'spirit of fear'.[12]

Then there is the fear associated with physical pain. The pain of childbirth[13] illustrated by Rachel in 'severe labour',[14] the pain of strenuous physical work, making the Israelites, when slaves in Egypt, 'groan' in pain.[15] Stephen was in pain from stoning[16] as was Paul.[17] Paul with others, endured the pain of flogging[18] (their wounds needing attention). But, worst of all was the physical suffering and pain endured by the Lord Jesus on the Cross; the thorns pressed into his head, the hammering, the pounding of the nails into hands and feet, the torn flesh as the weight of his body pulled on those nailed hands. Crucifixion was a cruel, agonising way to die. Bones out of joint, heart like wax, mouth dried like a potsherd, tongue sticking to the jaws, hands and feet pierced, shrivelled so that the bones could be counted,[19] stricken, smitten, slaughtered, wounded, crushed.[20] And death came slowly. Yet, the only words from the Cross were of forgiveness, no cry of pain, 'like a lamb led to the slaughter is silent'. It is for us to try to imagine the pain: 'Were you there when they crucified my Lord?' More than physical pain of course – the mental, spiritual pain of carrying the burden of the sin of the world. 'wounded for our transgressions, bruised for our iniquities'. An upset, wounded heart indeed. And, at the end it was a sword-thrust through the heart.

What then is the biblical answer to fear, to trouble, to pain, to the 'upset heart'? A good place to start is in the psalms, the 'open picture of the human heart'. A good example is Psalm 27 which begins with that question from David, 'whom shall I fear?' a question which is then repeated (in poetry, a device known as 'synonymous parallelism'). Then in the following verses a

10 Isaiah 51:12.
11 Proverbs 29:25.
12 2 Timothy 1:7.
13 Genesis 3:16.
14 Genesis 35:17.
15 Exodus 2:23; Nehemiah 9:9.
16 Acts 7:58.
17 Acts 14:19.
18 Acts 16:22, 23.
19 Psalm 22:14-17.
20 Isaiah 53:4, 5.

vivid crescendo of fear, fear of evildoers, enemies, adversaries, of an army encamped against him, a real physical battle ahead – or maybe simply in the mind since the phrase 'eat up my flesh' (v. 2) sounds like psychological disintegration, a mind devoured by fear. Then comes the confident answer to his troubled, fearful, upset heart, 'my heart shall not fear' (v. 3). And this is the answer to our fears too. It begins with prayer to the Lord ('one thing have I asked' v. 4), then his response to the invitation to 'seek God's face' (v. 8). Then there is the reminder of past help (v. 9) and the singing!

We do not know the occasion for the writing of this psalm, as with so many of David's contributions to the psalter, but E M Blaiklock surmises that this an early psalm, perhaps relating to David's battle with Goliath with the terror, the menace of a powerful foe. He would never forget that experience, the collapse of the giant in a crash of iron with the stone pebble implanted in his skull. So with us. Reminders of past help and the Lord's 'victories' in our lives strengthen us for the next battle – 'each victory will help you some other to win' as the old Sankey hymn has it. The key is David's trust in God, God will 'hide' him, God will 'lift him up', God will help, will teach, comfort, not forsake. Confidence wins out over trouble as he focuses on God. There is single mindedness here, 'one thing' (v. 4). There is obedience here too (v. 8 – 'you have said seek, that will I do'). In the day of trouble and of fear David has found refuge; hidden with God, in the secret place.

The word then from God's word about our fears, our troubles, the situations that 'upset' whatever they are, is 'be not afraid'. 'What time I am afraid I will trust in him'. This is not simply a piece of good advice it is a command of Jesus. 'Let not (do not let) your hearts be troubled neither let them be afraid'. Confidence in the One who can be trusted. Balm for the upset, troubled, fearful heart.

You could sing to yourself this lovely hymn on the next page about 'troubled (or anxious) hearts' by Timothy Dudley-Smith, appropriately entitled 'Set your troubled hearts at rest'.

SET YOUR TROUBLED HEARTS AT REST

'Set your troubled hearts at rest,'
hear again the word divine;
all our Father does is best;
let his peace be yours and mine.

Trusting still in God above,
set your troubled hearts at rest;
find within a Father's love
comfort for a soul distressed.

When you come to make request
know that God will answer prayer;
set your trouble hearts at rest,
safe within a Father's care.

Be at peace, then, and rejoice,
loved and comforted and blest;
hear again the Saviour's voice;
'Set your troubled hearts at rest.'

Timothy Dudley-Smith

V is for VULNERABLE – AGEING AND THE HEART

"'You are old, Father William," the young man said.'[1]

'My heart shall not fear'[2].

For some, especially the young, age is not a particularly interesting subject. As Groucho Marx had it, 'anyone can get old; all you have to do is to live long enough'. It is also no surprise to learn that the older we become the more likely we are to die. If you live in the UK and are a girl of eighteen reading this book (a most unlikely scenario) then your chance of dying in a year is less than 1 in 10,000, whereas if you are a man aged 70 the chance of remaining alive in that year decreases very significantly to only about 20 to 1. If you were fortunate to live in certain parts of Italy and have reached the age of 105 (as 4,000 did last year) then there is a 50/50 chance that you will die within the year. Statistics do not lie. Usually. But, how does one categorise age? Three subcategories may be distinguished: the 'young old' (age 65 to 75), the 'middle old' (age 75 to 85) and the 'very old' (over 85). Advances in medical treatment means that this last category has seen a large increase in numbers with resultant huge and increasing demands upon the health services.

It also comes as no surprise to learn that the older one gets the more vulnerable one becomes. And indeed, over the age of 60 years the frequency of cardiovascular disease accounts for at least 40% of all deaths. Certainly, ageing invariably leads to physical restrictions. There are things we can no longer do. We use steps rather than a chair to reach that top shelf, we cannot reach our toes to cut our toenails (hence the need of a good chiropodist), we can no longer run for the bus, failing to remember that there will be another one along soon. Sometimes! Standing for long periods (those prolonged worship times at church!) is more difficult, whilst talking (and listening)

---

1   Poem by Lewis Carroll that appears in his book, *Alice's Adventures in Wonderland*.
2   Psalm 27:3.

The key problem then of ageing, that 'emperor of all diseases', is the wear and tear of tissues throughout the body, when the building (anabolic) and destroying (catabolic) processes, held in balance over so many years, slide towards the over-preponderance of breakdown.

Then there are the mental vulnerabilities: concern for family members for whom we can now do much less than in earlier times, the fears of loneliness, of loss of memory, of losing our independence, the loss of old friends 'going before', the fear of not having the financial resources if ever we were to need care, of feeling unable to adapt to a rapidly changing world, with its emphasis on newer means of communication (that increasing number of new gadgets and 'updates'), of feeling 'cut off' from the environment that had been ours for so many years. These are all things that make us more vulnerable, that word derived from the Latin root meaning 'to wound', left open to attack, left unprotected from possible harm.

Another difficulty in ageing is the alteration in sleep patterns. Who else is awake at 3am? Doctors, midwives, BBC radio presenters and pilots. Many elderly experience 'microarousals' (up to a thousand times a night) – the opposite to those periods of 'microsleep'. So, there are disturbances in our time clock, in circadian rhythm; we fall asleep earlier and wake up earlier because of the effect of age on the body clock.

Our hearts, along with the rest of our body, are part of that inevitable decline, becoming more vulnerable as we age. After all, the heart is a pump and, as with any pump, time takes toll with the passing years; its performance becomes less efficient. The coronary vessels, supplying the heart with blood, lose their elasticity, due to earlier atherosclerotic changes, and become hardened, rather like an ageing rubber hose, making it more difficult for the blood to get through them. As a consequence, the arteries become less able to adequately supply the heart with the blood needed to enable the pump to work efficiently, or to compensate for rapid changes in myocardial oxygen demand, as in exercise. This natural history of coronary disease has been likened to a three-act dramatic tragedy. Act one introduces us to the main characters – hypertension and the progressive laying down of lipids in the vascular wall. In Act two the vascular wall is increasingly attacked, leading to deformation. Act three is the shortest of all: plaque rupture and the artery thromboses and the hero or heroine (usually the 'hero') succumbs, often unaware of the drama being enacted within their coronary arteries.

The decline in cardiac function with ageing is in part due to a shrinkage in cell size (atrophy), which occurs in all the 'vital' organs. Despite this there is an increase in the size and thickness of the ventricular wall (cardiac hypertrophy), a signal for developing heart failure, and a reduction in the size of the ventricular cavities, especially so in elderly females. In addition, disorders in cardiac rhythm are common in the elderly. The clinical presentation of symptoms may also change and this lack of 'typical symptoms' can sometimes lead to non-recognition of the condition. For example, fewer elderly patients present with 'typical' chest pain but instead more frequently complain of dyspepsia (sometimes with nausea and vomiting) and shortness of breath.

You do not have the same heart you had five years ago! This is because it is a self-renewing organ; there is a life-long regeneration of cardiac cells (myocytes) from progenitor (stem) cells that can self-renew or differentiate into myocytes, vascular smooth muscle or endothelial cells. Even bone marrow cells can traffic to the heart. This renewing process is less efficient in the ageing heart due, in the main, to a reduction in the synthesis of DNA and an unmodulated accumulation of calcium leading to DNA fragmentation. This makes the ageing heart more susceptible to ischaemic injury. Although stem cells are still present in the ageing heart many are senescent and unable to participate in the cell regenerating cycle or to aid repair and thus help in recovery from cellular damage. As yet, we do not know for certain if the injection of stem cells around an area of injury, such as might result from a myocardial infarction, can reduce the extent of the injury and improve ventricular function and ultimately prognosis.

We have dealt elsewhere with how diet can modify these changes in heart function. Is there anything else that can be done once the detrimental changes have occurred? We now enter the future! Recently scientists at my old *alma mater* (University College London) have explored, in experimental studies in mice, whether transfusing blood from young animals can rejuvenate the old. It can. Conversely, transfusing the blood of old mice caused ill health in the young. Already, blood plasma from teenage donors has been used to 'rejuvenate' ageing Silicon Valley billionaires – at a cost of $8000 for 2.7 litres. It is too soon to determine whether customers are wasting their money or not! The key ingredient appears to be a blood protein called GDF11. Some of us await further news with bated breath!

Yet, to quote Tennyson, 'Old age has yet his honour and his toil; death closes all; but something ere the end, some work of noble note may yet be done'. Or, even better, 'teach us to number our days that we may get a heart of wisdom'.[3]

Scripture has much to say about ageing. Vulnerability is the subject of Ecclesiastes chapter 12, 'the desolations of old age'. There are in this passage fearful concerns about the dangers of the streets, about burglary, safety, problems of balance and the fear of falling, the loss of the ability to sing and to sleep, the slowness of step and memory, the difficulty in making decisions. There are good examples of this in Scripture – Samuel, David, Solomon, Hezekiah, Josiah all found decisions difficult to make later in life. It is all here, the pointed reminder of decay and of the brave struggle to survive.

A sad example of ageing in Scripture is that of King David. When nearing death this once shrewd military leader, organiser and administrator, showed he was no longer able to make decisions or to lead his country. He simply could not make up his mind, which is one of the characteristic mental features of many old people. King David's experience also demonstrates one of the key effects on the heart and circulation of ageing; he just could not keep warm.[4] Despite covering him with clothes he was blue with cold, an effect of a failure of the circulation to meet the needs of his ageing body. Any remedy? Well, today we do have electric blankets and vasodilator drugs to open up those closed (constricted) blood vessels in the extremities. Those who were given the task of keeping David warm, when heaps of bed clothes proved insufficient, could think of only one thing. Get the old man an attractive entrancing young girl who would 'cherish him and minister to his needs'.[5]

It would have worked in the past (remember Abigail and Bathsheba) but not this time. Even the beautiful young Abishag the Shunammite attempts to arouse the king were unsuccessful. He still 'gat no heat', no spark of life in David. He could no longer make love to the beauty queen of Palestine: 'he knew her not'. A mind confused and a body weak. The test then of his cardiovascular (and hormonal) adequacy had failed. He simply did not make the grade. And the sad thing about David's situation was that he was apparently not what we would call really old. Ageing can begin early.

3   Psalm 90:12.

4   1 Kings 1:1.

5   1 Kings 1:2-4.

Is there too a spiritual vulnerability with ageing? Sometimes. There is one tragic, indeed frightening, scriptural example of this and a warning for all of 'a certain age', those of us who 'have been young but now are old'.[6] This is the story of the 'old prophet' who lived in Bethel.[7] In this story we see the apparent jealousy of someone, an ageing servant, once active for God ('a prophet') for someone younger, more spiritual and more courageous than himself. The danger of complacency, slackness in old age and seemingly, a decay in his spiritual life and service. A warning and the need for an even greater reliability on the Lord who is able to sustain 'to the end'.

The other references to old men in Scripture are more encouraging! Caleb is an example of the vitality of an ageing population, of 'grey power', a project created by the Dutch artist Yoni Lefevre. He invited schoolchildren to attempt to sketch their grandparents; many of the resultant drawings reflected their impressions of 'lively' elders – gardening, painting, playing tennis; active, exploring new activities. 'Grey power' indeed! Caleb illustrated this kind of vitality well into his senior years. As a young man he was one of the 'spies', the representatives of each tribe who infiltrated the occupied land for a six-week inspection tour of the land God had promised (Numbers chapter 13). It was agreed by all that this was a wonderful land[8] but the majority conclusion, as is often the case, was against attempting to 'go up' and possess it. This was because of fear (v. 32, 33) and unbelief ('we are not able' v. 31). One wonders how old these 'spies' were; fear and lack of confidence are two common attitudes of older people. In contrast, Caleb's response was positive 'do not fear, the Lord is with us'. Let's go! As often happens, the majority report led to many wasted years.

Forty-five years later Caleb, now eighty-five and still following the Lord,[9] was as strong, or so he said, as he was in his younger years. He requested a tough, somewhat risky task – 'give me this mountain where the cities are great and fenced'. Not much wrong with his physical heart, all that exercise involved in forty years of wandering in the desert and that 'ceaseless toil'. Nor of his spiritual heart for that matter. His faith, never wavering, had strengthened his healthy physical heart. As Paul Brand wrote 'how dare you talk of not taking risks? – old age is the time to take risks! Being old is bad

---

6   Psalm 37:25.

7   1 Kings 13:11-32.

8   Numbers 13:26, 27.

9   Joshua 14:6-14.

enough but to allow him (or her) to become helpless and require others to wait on them is unconscionable!' Inside every old person is a young person wondering what is happening!

And, as Timothy Dudley-Smith reminds us about the future; 'My times are in your hands; and I would not change that Lord. Although I see new experiences ahead, a time to 'lay things down', the scene contracting, work beyond my powers'. And then the prayer – 'Let me learn, now, to trust myself to your safe keeping, as once I learned (to trust myself to swim)'. The answer to the vulnerability of ageing is just that; 'Lord, to be ready unresisting, in calm and peace and joy, to float upon your tide'. 'Even to your old age . . . I am he who will sustain you. I have made you and I will carry you'.[10] And underneath are the everlasting arms!

---

10 Isaiah 46:4.

W is for the WORRIED, STRESSED HEART

Jesus said, 'Don't worry![1]
'Pray and let God worry.'[2]

Having attempted the subject of anxiety why, I wondered, am I now thinking about worry? Is there a difference and, if so, what is it? Am I being pedantic in separating them? Is it that I could not think of another suitable word beginning with W? Well, what about wounded?

It is true that the word 'worry' seldom appears in Scripture and, depending on the various English translations, the most relevant passages of Scripture, or so I thought, come in Matthew[3] and the similar passage in Luke[4] with the command, and it is certainly that, 'Don't worry' (NIV, JBP) or 'do not be anxious' (as in the ESV). After returning to Scripture, I then remembered that somewhere on my bookshelves is a book entitled appropriately *The Worry Book*.[5] But where was that book? I became worried that I could not find the worry book! When eventually it was discovered I found that the, almost only, passage of the New Testament discussed was the one in Matthew and from that, I was relieved to find, the authors also concluded 'that there are very few references to worry in the Bible'. Then comes a helpful exposition of this passage.

The word in Greek is *merimnao* which (probably) means to distract, to draw in different directions and thus 'to be careful for' (a care that distracts) or 'to take thought', to be insecure. The opposing negative adjective signifies 'free from care' or to be 'secure'. Our gifted translators seemed to have difficulty with this word; in the Luke passage the ESV

---

1   Matthew 6:25.

2   Martin Luther.

3   Matthew 6:25-34.

4   Luke 12:22-31.

5   W. van der Hart and R. Waller, *The Worry Book: Finding a Path to Freedom*, Inter-Varsity Press 2010.

uses 'be anxious' in verses 22, 25 and 26 but 'worried' in verse 29! Moffatt uses the word 'trouble' and Eugene Peter Peterson in the Message has words like 'be worked up about', 'fuss', 'preoccupied with' whilst in Scots it is 'binna sair thochtit' or 'thochtiness' (linked with 'to think') in the passage in Luke. Just right! It is interesting to observe how other European languages translate the original.

Is this simply being pedantic? Is 'worry' of a different order to 'being anxious'? Perhaps 'worry' has a sense of lingering or continuously dwelling on something, of brooding, a persistent and deep anxiety, a conviction, a dread almost of certain (or possible) harm. It means to fret (as comes, for example, three times in Psalm 37 'fret not'), a helpless, wasted thought process which can often give rise to stress. If so, then perhaps there is an example of this in the story of Mary and Martha in Luke.[6] I sense that the visit of Jesus to their home was beginning to prey on the mind of Martha. Jesus was such a good friend but also, of course, he was someone really special and she wanted, quite rightly, the very best for him. A woman reading this will know what I mean! She may have been thinking about this visit for days. Then there would be the visits to the markets, much thought about food selection and maybe that haggle over price, part of the whole market experience. Only the very best food, and the way it was cooked, would be good enough for him. Yet, as Jesus said, 'you are worried and troubled about many (ongoing) things'.[7] Well, she might have thought, there really are so many things to think about, I have been worried about this ever since I knew you were coming, maybe even for days! Even necessity can be a distraction. I can feel the stress building up! Note the contrast between the 'many things' and 'this one thing' in the next verse.[8] A right thing but in the wrong spirit at the wrong time. Perhaps the following may have been in her mind?

Lord of all pots and pans and things, since I've no time to be
A saint by doing lovely things, or watching late with Thee,
Or dreaming in the dawn light, or storming heaven's gates –
Make me a saint by getting meals and washing up the plates!

---

6 Luke 10:38-42.

7 Luke 10:41.

8 Luke 10:42.

Yet later it is from this same Martha that we have the most sure testimony of almost anyone in Scripture to the person of Christ – 'I believe that you are the Christ, the Son of God, the One coming into the world and I know that whatever you ask of God, God will give it to you'.[9]

'One thing is needful' – in our much serving and multi-tasking perhaps we make life too complicated. That 'one thing' is the quality of our time with God and our concern for God's glory. 'Seek first'.

How many times in our own lives have we dwelt on something - care of family, the health of loved ones (or our own health) financial affairs, travel plans – and lain awake at night, unable to sleep, with these 'things' on our minds. Or concerns about the future. Worried. Troubled. I sometimes think about the Holy Family on route to Bethlehem from Nazareth at a time when Mary was heavily pregnant, and what must have been on Joseph's mind at the time. The risks taken, the 'what might happen' on that journey – and thereafter. Worried if they would make it, their safety on a potentially dangerous road, possible infection in the stable, then the flight as refugees into a foreign land with such a young child. What might happen to this so precious burden? So many things on his mind. But, of course, they were doing the Father's will, obeying that voice and therefore could be left in God's protective hands. Nothing was going to thwart God's purposes. Nor God's purposes for us.

Before we leave the subject of 'worry' we should think about what it might lead to if not dealt with. Worry as a forerunner of stress.

It seems that more than 75% of patients with a heart condition feel 'stressed'; they become obsessive about diet, they feel anger (why me?), lose confidence and find daily duties, the normal routine, difficult. But what is 'stress'? It is intense pressure or tension, originally used of the strain on a mechanical (and physical) structure. Hans Selye, who pioneered stress research in the 1960's, defined it as 'not what happens to you but how you react to it'. Selye showed that this stress response impacts on almost every body organ system. For example, it impacts on the functions of the digestive system; 'butterflies' when taking an exam, facing an interview or preaching in an unknown church. This is all part of the communication between the gastrointestinal tract and the brain. And, this is bi-directional; gastrointestinal illness is often accompanied by neuropsychiatric symptoms such as anxiety or even depression.

---

9 John 11:27.

Lazarus (not the Lazarus who died twice) suggests the following as a definition for negative stress: 'A condition, or a feeling, experienced when a person perceives that (external) demands exceed the personal and social resources that individual is able to mobilise'. Some of the demands of stress can be positive. It is not all bad news. It can motivate us to tackle a challenge, it can push us, encourage us to do things we would normally not attempt. Such stress, in small amounts (what Selye called 'eustress') can even enhance cognitive abilities, boost mental prowess, enabling us to focus more clearly. It may even improve memory. Promotion or success at work (or play), getting married or going on holiday are, usually, positive; they are, in Selye's stress categories 'eustressors', not to be confused with EUstress, which is a different form of stress altogether, especially for the UK Government! Eustressors are good stressors, making the heart happy. We could add perhaps that for some playing the piano, writing poetry or making jam are such. And, we should remember that there are very few people walking the streets today who are under no pressure at all; a blood pressure of 130/65 is fine, but a pressure of 0/0 is something else!

However, for most of us stress is negative, and those demands made upon us really can exceed our internal resources. These demands seem to have increased both with time and with age. Someone in their eighties opined 'life was easier in the old days, our lives were certainly less stressful, we did not even know what stress was'. Strange perhaps since such folk went through the war years. Are we then now busier, is the speed of life increasing and do we expect a more immediate personal response to life's challenges? Is it then a new word for the 20th or 21st century?

Stress levels are certainly dependent on the severity of external demands. Of course, highest of all on the stress list arise from the death of a spouse, a close relative or friend. Imprisonment, having our home damaged by flooding or by fire (as in the Grenfell disaster), burglary, unexpected financial problems, loss of one's job and serious illness, especially involving hospitalisation, come high on the list of 'stressors'. Commuter delays and starting a new job are apparently higher stressors than, for example, losing your mobile phone, terrorist threats or leaving the European Union.

However, what concerns us here are the effects of stress on the heart. One study has estimated that nearly 30% of acute myocardial infarctions can be attributed to psychosocial factors and that this form of stress rates higher than smoking or obesity. It is here that we have to distinguish between acute and chronic stress. First, acute stress and the heart. Anger, excitement and environmental events such as war, earthquakes and man-made terrorist attacks, have been shown to increase the risk of myocardial infarction and life-threatening disorders of cardiac rhythm. Personal tragedy is also associated with increased mortality. During bereavement the risk of a cardiac event is highest during the first month especially in those with pre-existing cardiac disease.

Chronic stress involving heart-related death and illness, is associated with traditional risk factors such as poor physical and mental health, poor nutrition and low socioeconomic status (which is made up of a person's occupation, wealth, education and social power). Limited or no access to medical care and exercise habits, or lack of them, are also major predictors of cardiovascular health. Occupation and marital stress are more pronounced risk factors in women than in men especially in those with few personal resources and high personal vulnerabilities. The experience of emotional stress associated with conflict and confrontation is a particularly important mental and cardiac stressor. Such situations do occur in church divisions; one elderly woman became particularly anxious when it was discovered that her funeral arrangements could not be made in the church to which she had belonged for most of her life because of a church 'split'. Church division is the cause of both emotional and, one presumes, cardiac stress; for Christian people church division is high on the list of negative stressors.

Stress is not to my knowledge, a biblical word although the related word pressure (tension) certainly is. Are there situations in Scripture that might be called stressed or pressurised if they were to happen today? And how if so, are these words related to scriptural words like anxiety (care), trouble, worry, unease, perplexity and fear? Perhaps there are at least two quite different situations that one could best describe as being potentially 'stressful', one example from each of the two testaments.

A possible example from the Old Testament comes in the well-known story of Jacob and Esau to be found in Genesis (Genesis 25 to 27). Jacob had left home years before, having stolen, 'taken away' by deception, his older brother Esau's birth right,[10] which Esau had previously despised.[11] Even more important, he had taken their father's 'blessing', which involved lands and family. Jacob did this, encouraged by his mother Rebekah, by

---

10 Genesis 27:1-30.
11 Genesis 25:32, 34.

pretending to be Esau and thus deceiving his aged, almost blind father. Now, years later, he was about to meet Esau again, the brother who hated him, who had threatened to kill him and who was the cause of Jacob's flight from home and long absence from his family.[12] Now they were to meet again with the anticipation that something dangerous and terrifying was around the corner. No wonder Jacob was greatly afraid and distressed.[13] Why, in this verse is there a duplication of verbs? What is the difference between fear and distress? In English the word 'distress' has the sense of physical exhaustion and extreme want. Jonathan Sacks suggests that this was a moral anxiety, the fear that during a battle he would be killed; distressed because he might kill someone, his brother perhaps.

This was a long and arduous journey for Jacob, with so much time on his mind concerning what lay ahead, both for him and his accompanying large family. So much time to think about what might happen. Apprehension, fear, distress and anxiety, all despite God's call to him to go and meet up with his brother,[14] the assurance of the Lord's presence with him (God 'would do him good')[15] and his own prayer for deliverance.[16] In such a situation today, I think the word 'stress' would be foremost in our minds! I am reminded of the prayer the Chaplain for the New York Fire Service said each time he went out to an emergency. The prayer would, of necessity, be very brief, all there was time for in an emergency – 'Lord, take me where you want me to go, may I meet the people you want me to meet, give me the words to say' and, I would add, the ear to listen. He was the first to die in 9/11. How did Jacob cope? Well, he had met with the Lord both at Bethel and later at the Jabbok ford, Jacob alone with his God at the place called Penuel, a 'miracle of grace in an unexpected place'. And that limp would be a permanent reminder of that life-changing meeting. After that there is no reference to 'fear'.

But just how did Jacob cope with this situation of stress? Firstly, and perhaps this came suddenly, was the realisation of how he had treated his brother by his deception and how truly monstrous his crime had been, now escalating into a life and death situation. What made it so? It was because

---

12 Genesis 27:41-43.

13 Genesis 32:7.

14 Genesis 31:3.

15 Genesis 32:12.

16 Genesis 32:11.

a patriarchal blessing[17] was not simply a farewell but it solemnly, inviolably transferred all the privileges that belonged to the clan successor, now not to Esau but to Jacob. This action of Jacob, and the decision of their father Isaac, was to have effects that reverberated throughout the rest of their lives. This sense of shame as to how he had treated his brother brought about a change that we might rightly call penitence. Notice Jacob's first response as he came near to his brother[18] bowing himself to the ground seven times, attempting to appease 'my lord Esau' with all those presents.[19]

Secondly, there were practical preparations for this crucial meeting, elaborate, almost like a ritual. Courteous, generous (all those sheep!), the arrangements of his large family; servants first, then Leah and her family and then Rachel, his favourite wife and himself last of all. This deep practical concern to look after his own. Thirdly, there was prayer ('deliver me').[20] A combination then of penitence, persistence, practical preparation and prayer.

And, where was God in all this? Well, God intervened. This meeting began with God. It involved Jacob alone with his maker not once but twice, first at Mahanaim then at Penuel.[21] The initiative was always with God. And, these meetings were not without, for Jacob, a struggle, a wrestling.

And what a reconciliation! What a surprise. If you read this story without knowing the ending you would never guess the outcome – Esau 'ran to meet him and fell on I face and kissed him, and they wept'. Jacob quite 'bowled over'. A wonderful ending to a great story. Only those within whose families there have been rifts and separations can experience the wonder of something similar. A dim picture of our own reconciliation with our heavenly Father through the person and work of Jesus.[22] Was this story of Jacob and Esau in Jesus' mind I wonder when he told the parable of the lost son?

We must not forget in this, one of the most dramatic of Old Testament stories, that stress was also on the father, Isaac. He had lost not one son but two. Jacob was gone, whilst Esau now took as wife a Canaanite woman

---

17 Genesis 27:26-29.
18 Genesis 33:3.
19 Genesis 32:13-20.
20 Genesis 32:11.
21 Genesis 32:24-31.
22 Romans 5:10, Ephesians 2:16.

which did not please him and caused friction within the family. One can imagine the difficulties this caused within Isaac's household. Certainly, family conflict, the cause of long-term stress for all concerned. Did this situation one wonders hasten his death?

The word 'stress' also does not appear as such in the New Testament but the word for pressure (*epistasis*) does. Paul, after recounting the physical external trials in his life[23] tells about 'the daily pressure on me of my anxiety for all the churches' including 'the danger from false brothers'. Phillips translates this 'the daily burden of responsibility', the pastoral things that crowded upon him day to day. This was both a daily pressure for all the churches, not only the ones known to him personally but some far distant, many he had never visited. Alan Redpath puts this well – 'I could not possibly convey adequately' he writes, 'the force of this statement – that which cometh upon me daily' – and likens this stress to being smothered by a blanket or being crushed by some great animal. Perhaps we can get close to the force of this word (*epistasis*) by recalling the incident recorded in Arthur Miller's great play 'The Crucible' concerning the death of Giles Cory. Giles was falsely accused of conversing with the devil. It tells how he was 'pressed': 'Great stones they lay upon his chest until he plead aye or nay. They say he gave them two words. "More weight," he says. And died'. Pressure!

Paul's words convey his huge pastoral heart. One wonders if this is also so conveyed in today's church. There is a temptation to separate the ministry of the word ('I am here solely to preach') from pastoral care, left often to others. I wonder where this comes from? Paul might ask can these be separated? For him this pastoral care was with him always, no vacation from it ever, the care, compassionate concern for all the churches. A burden that went right around the world. A burden that could not be shaken off. Feeling daily the pressure, the stress.

To end this chapter on a positive note! The only other time this same word comes is where it is used of 'stirring up', making a stir, 'pressing on'.[24] 'Let us press on'. Let us 'keep on going on'.[25] A kind of eustress! The positive effect of 'stress'.

---

23 2 Corinthians 11:26-28.

24 Philippians 3:12, 14.

25 Hebrews 6:1.

X is for the UNKNOWN, the CROSS and LOVE

'I found this inscription . . . to an unknown god . . .
him I proclaim to you.'[1]

'I know the one in whom I have placed my confidence'.[2]

Perhaps those of you who have got this far may now be looking forward to a blank page and a rest from words. What can we make of X? There are no words beginning with X in the Bible and none, as far as I am aware, that refer to the heart apart from X-rays. However, X, the twenty-fourth letter of the English alphabet, is a very ubiquitous letter as we shall see. Just think what it can stand for:

X is the number for ten (10) in Latin

X in mathematics means 'to multiply'.

X marks who or what you want to vote for, or in place of a name when you are unable to write.

X marks the spot on a map to indicate position.

X stands for a kiss and therefore for love.

X can, albeit rarely, stand for xero (or zero) and could thus stand for death (xero life) thus 'love (X) is as strong as death (X)'[3] whilst *xeno* is a prefix for something strange or foreign (such as xenophobia)

X is a cross, indeed the cross of crucifixion, in some cultures or at certain times, limbs stretched out, opened out, not the *crux immissa* of the familiar two beams but the *crux decussata* – the St. Andrew's cross as in the Scottish flag and the Union Jack.

X in geometry is a coordinate, and in algebra, $x+y=2$ is a straight line and $x2+y2=1$ is a circle.

X can stand for anything (or anyone) unknown.

---

1   Acts 17:23.

2   2 Timothy 1:12.

3   Song of Solomon 8:6.

X for some, can even stand for Christ – as in Xmas, a quite unnecessary 'abbreviation'.

Xer (from the Greek) is a prefix meaning dry. Thus, xeroderma is a morbid dryness of the skin or a dryness of the spirit, of waterless springs[4] or like a dry and waste land where there is no water.[5] It can also stand for 'hard'. After all, the greatest enemy to faith is not doubt but numbness, indifference, unfeeling – dead, dryness. Can this, I wonder, refer to the heart? A kind of *xerokardia*, not a word you will find in the Oxford or standard medical dictionaries but perhaps describing a condition (as yet, as far as I am aware, undiscovered!) where there is a loss of pericardial fluid such that the outer surface of the heart is 'dry', not lubricated.

Of these various possibilities three stand out because they have some possible link with the heart – X for unknown, X for the cross and X for love.

X is for the unknown

The young Francis Crick was always asking questions and decided, after reading a children's encyclopaedia, to become a scientist. He had one worry. That science had already made so many discoveries – would there be any left for him? As his mother told him 'when you grow up there will be plenty left for you to discover. How about 'what is life' and how is it passed on?' It led several years later to his participation in the discovery of the structure of DNA as a double helix and the award nine years later of the Nobel Prize for Medicine.

I look back on almost fifty years of biomedical research and in the 1950's, as today, there was much that was 'unknown' but which is now 'known'. In 1956 as a PhD student I was working on histamine, an endogenous substance found in certain cells in the body called 'mast cells' and which is released following tissue injury. I read in the scientific literature about substances manufactured by a French pharmaceutical company (Rhone Poulenc) that were said to antagonise ('block') the effects of histamine; they were therefore 'antihistamines'. I wrote, pen, ink and paper in those far-off days, to the author, one Dr J.L. Parot, to see if he could supply me with a small amount of these 'RP compounds'. My 'almost namesake' wrote back, enclosing them, and wondered if we were related (actually there are French ancestors in the

---

4   2 Peter 2:17.

5   Psalm 63:1.

family). These RP substances were said to block special binding sites for histamine (called 'receptors') on the membranes of some cells and that they did this without antagonising the effects of other endogenous substances like adrenaline. So, they were reasonably specific. And useful.

Later discovered antihistamines however had rather unfortunate side effects. I was at one time teaching medical students about histamine. This involved injecting it under the skin to demonstrate the 'triple response' – initially described many years ago by Sir Thomas Lewis – reddening (flushing, due to vasodilatation), a wheal (oedema, which we now know is not a direct effect), and a flare surrounding the injection site with a resultant rise in skin temperature. Those who have been stung by nettles can observe these same three effects plus itching, which is yet another effect of histamine since nettles are 'histamine releasers'.

Some of the students were first given an antihistamine drug, after which the injection of histamine did not elicit the 'triple response'. Unfortunately for these students the antihistamine used had side effects (all drugs have these) and this included drowsiness. The evening of that particular class was the annual student ball which these particular students did not fully enjoy! Many complaints the following week! However, at least they did learn something about the effects of histamine and of the drugs that block its actions through 'histamine receptors'. And, this a really important lesson, that all drugs have more than one effect on the body. I should hasten to add that this is an oversimplification. Histamine acts on more than one receptor type and hence has several other actions which include an increase in the force of contraction of the heart and the stimulation of acid gastric juice.

This concept of receptors goes back to Paul Ehrlich in the early part of the twentieth century. He surmised that endogenous substances (and drugs) must be 'bound' in some way to the external surface of body cells in order to produce an effect. His dictum was '*corpora non agunt nisi fixata*'; a drug will not work unless it is bound. In those far off days we knew nothing about 'what happens next', how the message traverses the cell wall (called transduction) and results in something happening inside the cell itself. Now, fifty years after those simple experiments with histamine, we know so much more about what receptor types are involved in the actions of drugs and also about 'what happens next'. The point is that what was unknown fifty years ago is now common knowledge, at least among some scientists.

But there is still much that is unknown including about the heart (I could elucidate). So, the X for unknown is still with us.

How does this relate to knowledge of God? Is there a theological X? Can God really be known? Surely, man cannot hope to know the One who created and sustains the universe(s), the indescribable, uncontainable, all powerful, amazing God? Can we be open to the 'mystery of God'? As the psalmist wrote, 'what is man that you regard him, that you think of him'?[6] and in the book of Job, 'the Almighty – we cannot find him';[7] when Moses requested to see God, the response was to hide him in a cleft of a rock so that he could see only his back[8] and touch just the hem of his garments. There is much about God that is unknown. He is still, in one sense, the 'unknown God'.

Of course, God knows us; 'what is man that you are mindful of him, that you care for him?'[9] God knows everything about us. But the reverse? Can man by searching find out God? Can he be known by any man? Is it possible for mortals in this dark world of shadows to have fellowship with the Almighty? As I write there is great excitement among astronomers because there are eight radio telescopes around the world coming together to focus, with wonderful clarity, on a 'black hole'. But, as someone said, is God 'out there' too? Can we see him? A lot of preparation went into that particular scientific experiment but any preparation for seeing God is of a different kind. God is not a material 'thing'. We cannot learn of him, let alone know him, with our material sense perception. But can we find him and know him?

Paul, in a visit to Athens and awaiting the arrival of his co-workers Silas and Timothy[10] saw in a tour of the city, that it was full of idols. He was invited to speak to the Athenian philosophers, among whom were Epicurean materialists whose belief was that the world happened by chance, a random concourse of atoms, mindless, purposeless, accidental. The Epicureans have not yet disappeared; they are still with us, 'scientists' mainly sitting in their armchairs writing!

Paul started by perceiving that the men of Athens (no mention here of the women) were very religious with 'many objects of worship'. However, the altar that especially interested Paul was 'to an unknown God'. To the

6 Psalm 144:3.
7 Job 37:23.
8 Exodus 33:18-23.
9 Psalm 8:4.
10 Acts 17:15.

Athenians then there was a God who was unknown, so it is possible that they realised there may be something (someone?) beyond their Hellenic gods, an absentee god. They wanted to cover all the options! What a good background introduction for proclaiming the God whom they could know! 'Whom you ignorantly worship, him I declare to you'.[11] Or, as Phillips translates this verse, 'this God I am here to proclaim to you'. The days are over for groping in the darkness and searching in the shadows. Over too time for excuses.

It is an extraordinary thing to claim to 'know God'. Not just knowledge about God but to have direct contact with God. The claim is quite staggering. Is this not foolish, mistaken, a self-deception? Can God be known in such a way by any man? Yet many millions of people through the centuries have found this 'knowledge' gloriously true! However, this is not to imply that, although we can know God in the sense of understanding how to come into his family and have a relationship with him, we know all there is to know about him. God remains a mystery, we can only know what God has revealed about himself, 'the things that are revealed belong to us but the secret things belong to the Lord our God'.[12]

There are things hidden from us, unknown. How, for example, is it possible that God is both personal to us yet transcendent? How is time related to eternity? How can One God be triune? How can a good God allow so much evil in this world, so much suffering? What God has not disclosed we cannot know; we can only ponder the limits set down. We can, as with science, understand just so much. God is still, in so many ways, the 'unknown God' to whom we need to respond with faith. Only some things about God have been revealed. But that is enough. And that verse in Deuteronomy should be written and placed on the desk of every theologian and scientist, every student of God's word.

We could start with the experience of folk of old 'knowing God' as recorded in the Bible. King David's command to his son Solomon was 'to know the God of your father' and 'to serve him with a whole heart and a willing mind'; 'if you seek him, he will be found by you'.[13] David here speaks from experience. 'Be still and know that I am God'.[14] The psalms are full of the experiences of 'knowing God' and enjoying the reality of

11 Acts 17:23.
12 Deuteronomy 29:29.
13 1 Chronicles 28:9.
14 Psalm 46:10.

his presence.[15] Just one example. David in Psalm 36 speaks of God's love, faithfulness, righteousness, justice, salvation and then asks God, this God whom he knows, to 'continue your loving-kindness to those who know you'. So, we are to 'know the Lord'.[16]

However, knowing God in what way? It is Jesus who has made God known, has revealed to us how we can know God. 'Jesus, in the bosom of the Father, who has lived in the closest intimacy with God the Father, he has declared him, 'made him known'[17] shown us how much we are loved by him.[18] So, we can know God, know what he is like and know him for ourselves if 'we seek him with all our heart'. This is the heart of the Christian faith. It is not just knowing something about God, good though that is, but having a personal relationship with him; it means to 'come' to him[19] and to be indwelt by him.[20]

How is this possible? Only because this 'unknown God' makes himself known to us. For us to 'find' God is impossible; this can only come because this revelation, this knowledge, is from God himself and from him only. It is a work of love that is called grace. As Isaiah wrote of God 'I have chosen you that you might know and believe me and understand that I am he'.[21] To know God is to have an intimate, experiential, involving, knowledge; the Hebrew word (*yada*) means to know by observation and reflection, by thinking; and it is the heart that plays an important role in this. This knowledge can come gradually, often as a result of quietness, the silent contemplation of Scripture and through prayer. Or it can come dramatically – as with John Wesley 'I felt my heart strangely warmed'. Or, as with me, at a University Mission in London in November 1953. The 'unknown' suddenly and dramatically becomes known.

X is for the Cross, for crucifixion

'Certainly, some science can be learned in the head, but the knowledge of Christ crucified can only be learnt by the heart' (Spurgeon).

---

15 Psalm 23:4.
16 Jeremiah 31:34; Hosea 2:20; Hebrews 8:11.
17 John 1:18.
18 John 3:16.
19 John 6:65.
20 John 14:20.
21 Isaiah 43:10.

Crucifixion places an enormous strain on the heart due to the fixed position of the body and the intense pain; indeed, the pain suffered is excruciating (which comes from the word crucifixion) and is accentuated by the loss of blood from the broken limbs and of fluid from sweating in the hot Palestinian climate. Crucifixion also makes it difficult to breathe deeply; breath comes in short gasps. Perhaps this is the reason for the brevity of the seven last words from the Cross; none in English is more than ten words and the last four, like gasps, have very few words indeed, just two ('I thirst') and then just one, a shout of triumph, 'Finished!', 'Completed!', 'Accomplished!'

Crucifixion was used extensively by the Romans, although not invented by them. Only slaves and the lowest type of criminal were crucified, rarely Roman citizens (probably Peter was crucified but Paul beheaded). It was a symbol of humiliation and shame, of curse and offence.[22] Yet, the Cross of Christ is central to the Christian Faith. It is used as a description of salvation. 'Christ died (on the Cross) for our sins' stands for the gospel,[23] the news of our salvation; our redemption comes through his blood shed on the Cross.[24] The death of Christ on the Cross atones. It is the heart of the gospel; 'we preach Christ and Christ crucified' wrote Paul to the Corinthian church.[25] He made a decision to 'know nothing among you except Christ and him crucified'[26] so it was Paul's 'secret determination to concentrate entirely on Jesus Christ himself and the fact of his death upon the cross' (Phillips). Paul 'gloried', boasted in the Cross of our Lord Jesus Christ.[27] 'If the world had known it would not have crucified the Lord of Glory'.[28]

It is the power of the Cross to draw individuals to faith in Christ, 'I when I am lifted up' – the word that led me to faith in Christ.[29] In Charles Wesley's words, ''Tis Love, 'tis Love! Thou diedst for me, I hear the whisper in my heart'. And it is from the wounded heart of Christ that the church came forth. In the words of St Francis, 'Jesus let my heart be pierced by that blade that transfixed your heart.'

---

22 Galatians 5:11.
23 1 Corinthians 15:3.
24 Ephesians 1:7.
25 1 Corinthians 1:23.
26 1 Corinthians 2:2.
27 Galatians 6:14.
28 1 Corinthians 2:8.
29 John 3:14; 12:32.

X is for love

How many times I wonder have we received a card or letter at the foot of which is this letter X, perhaps the first letter of the alphabet young children attempt to write, the symbol too of the touch with the lips to show love. It goes beyond mere formality. It binds one person to another by ties of the heart, it speaks of devotion, of a depth of feeling, it goes beyond mere attachment, it is more than a warm feeling towards, it denotes the emotion a person feels for someone (or something). It goes beyond affection in intensity. Truly loving another is characterised by kindness, patience, tolerance, forgiveness, thankfulness and humility.[30] It is 'the golden chain of all the virtues'.

As Aristotle believed, this love comes from the heart, the 'centre of man, that inner fire that gives both warmth and light'; 'the heart is everything and everything is in the heart'. From the Middle Ages the heart became a symbol both of sacred and earthly, carnal love. As one German song of the troubadours has it – 'you are mine, I am yours, you must be sure of that, you are enclosed in my heart, its little key is lost so you must stay forever'! The language of the heart can ever reach another heart whereas mere words often don't get past your listener's ears. Listen to the heart! And in the eighteenth century, for poets and novelists the heart, now enlarged, became the organ where all passion is born, the love 'of a man for a maid' or as Verlaine put it (in the best written language of the heart) 'my faithful heart, just for you will it beat'.

In Scripture, as one might expect, love is a key word (in Hebrew *ahab* or *aheb*). It comes frequently, nearly three hundred times in the Old Testament alone. Here it has the sense of having a strong emotional attachment and a desire to either possess, or to be in the presence of, someone; of a man for a woman[31] or a woman for a man, parents for children, such as Abraham's love for his son Isaac,[32] or Ruth's love for her mother-in-law.[33] It is also used of an especially close attachment of friends, such as for David and Jonathan.[34] It carries with it a sense of loyalty.[35]

---

30 Colossians 3:12-14.
31 Genesis 29:20.
32 Genesis 22:2.
33 Ruth 1:16.
34 1 Samuel 18:1.
35 1 Kings 5:1.

In contrast to the single word for love used in Hebrew there are two distinct words for love in New Testament Greek and the difference between them is both significant and challenging. *Phileo*, like the Hebrew *ahab*, means to like, to have tender affection for and is used, for example, of the love of Jesus for the apostle John,[36] that is the one for whom Jesus had a special affection. In contrast, *agape* (and the corresponding verb *agapao*) is the 'characteristic word for Christianity'. Although it was not invented by Christians, they gave it a whole new meaning. It expresses ideas previously unknown since this is a love for someone for whom one does not have a particular affinity, indeed may even have no inclination to love, no particular feeling for. It is made out of deliberate choice and without any assignable cause. It seeks the welfare of all and the opportunity to do good to all.[37] One can see how challenging this is.

There is one interesting passage where both *agape* and *phileo* are used. This comes in the post-resurrection appearance of Jesus on the shore of the Sea of Tiberias.[38] After a fish breakfast with his disciples there is a conversation between Jesus and Peter; the threefold questions from Jesus are followed by Peter's answers. In almost all English versions the same word 'love' is used of both question and answer. However, both Greek words are used, *agape* by Jesus (except in the last of the three questions) but *phileo* by Peter. This is best brought out in the Phillips translation. In answer to the question 'do you love me?' (*agape*) Peter can only answer 'you know that I am your friend' (*phileo*). He cannot reach that same level of love that Jesus has for him. In the last question Jesus uses the same word (affection) that Peter has used – 'are you even my friend?' This, it seems to me, shows clearly the difference between these two New Testament words for love; *agape* for love that is unconditional and entirely free, expressed in giving, whilst *phileo* is the word for affectionate friendship. We shall see later how this relates to God's love for us.

---

36 John 20:2.
37 Galatians 6:10.
38 John 21:15-19.

Y is for YOUR EXAMINED HEART

'Let us test and examine our ways.'[1]

'Take care lest your heart be deceived.'[2]

'Search me O God and know my heart.'[3]

'What is the state if your heart' is both a clinical and spiritual question. Being an internal organ, it is not of course possible to see one's own heart. Others may see it; indeed, they need to, the cardiac surgeons during open heart surgery for example. Otherwise any examination to assess the function of the heart or to determine if there are signs of disease is, by necessity, indirect and often highly sophisticated. These, sometimes invasive, techniques determine how the heart is performing as a pump (the strength of the cardiac muscle driving blood into the vessels), how the valves between the atria and the ventricles and between the ventricles and the main vessels are functioning (if they are 'leaky' and incompetent) and to examine the state of the coronary vessels that supply the cardiac muscle with blood, which contains all that is necessary for that muscle to contract well.

Firstly, there are non-invasive techniques. These include auscultation (described in the chapter on L for listening), a chest X-ray (which determines, for example, whether the heart or large vessels are enlarged) and, because the heart generates electrical activity, measurements of the electrocardiogram (ECG). This will detect changes in heart rhythm and in the conduction of electrical impulses across the heart. The electrocardiogram is often assessed during exercise, for example during running on a treadmill or pedalling on a bicycle. Such tests are performed either in a cardiac clinic or during normal daily activity, by wearing lightweight monitoring equipment over a 24h period, or longer.

---

1   Lamentations 3:40.

2   Deuteronomy 11:16.

3   Psalm 139:23.

This is called Holter monitoring. This detects the characteristic changes in electrical activity of the heart for example when the blood supply is impaired.

Invasive techniques include cardiac catheterization. An appropriate catheter is inserted into a peripheral artery under aseptic conditions and then advanced into the right or left heart to measure pressure gradients, or into a coronary artery to assess, using contrast media, the condition of these arteries – how much obstruction, if any, there is to flow down these arteries due to the severity of atherosclerosis and the extent of vessel narrowing.

Another common technique to assess heart function is two-dimensional echocardiography. This depends on the analysis of high frequency sound waves directed at the heart from a transducer situated on the chest wall or across the oesophagus. Even more complicated is the use of magnetic resonance imaging, usually with a gadolinium contrast, and the use of biopsies. These are small pieces of cardiac muscle taken using a small needle at the end of a cardiac catheter, then followed by histological and biochemical analysis.

Any examination of the heart often begins as a consequence of self-examination, changes in body function ('doctor, something is not quite right') which, after a preliminary physical examination, would lead to the kinds of examination outlined above. I am reminded as I write these words of the announcements on ScotRail to contact a given emergency telephone number 'if you see something that does not look right'! So, what are these changes in body activity, of 'not feeling right', which may indicate a possible cardiac problem? They include breathlessness and/or chest pain on exertion, for example when walking uphill, or carrying shopping especially on a cold day and against the wind. Or even chest pain at rest? So, self-examination comes first!

Now these have spiritual parallels. Self-examination comes first. Each person is to examine himself.[4] This means careful enquiry, it involves a search, an investigation. Now I have a very clever laptop which examines itself. There are various tests it uses. The BT instructive test, the X87 Floating Point Test, the MMX test, the SSE test and the AES test, whatever these are! This at least suggests that there are various ways of 'self-examination' – certainly for the laptop – and this is true also of self-

---

4   1 Corinthians 11:28.

testing. We are to test and examine our ways[5] to 'see', to discern, to judge ourselves individually.

Firstly, we are to examine 'whether we are in the faith'[6] to see if Christ is in us by his Spirit. This is because 'the presence of the Spirit is the presence of Christ', Christ indwelling each believer. We must not fail this particular test. It may seem strange that Paul asks this crucial question at the very end of this letter; perhaps it was that this was the key question he wanted to leave in the hearts of the individual members of the Corinthian church. Do we really have faith or are we Christians in name only? No more important examination question than that. In Paul's first letter to this church the question was asked in the context of the Lord's Supper, in view the Lord's death, renewing the benefits of his death as a sacrifice for our sins. Accepting also that our fellowship is with other believers; in this context of corporate self-examination we do not normally eat and drink alone.

It is interesting that in the original Greek the word 'to examine' (*anakrisis*) is a legal term denoting a preliminary examination, an investigation with a view to gathering evidence. Note the word preliminary; just as in a physical examination we first submit ourselves to our own testing, gathering the evidence, to see if 'all is well' before we approach a physician. After all, 'he that is well has no need of a physician'.[7]

We then, after a self-examination, submit ourselves to the 'Great Physician'. We make this request. 'Examine me O Lord, prove me and test my heart' – the English Standard Version adds – 'and my mind'.[8] The writer bares his heart and mind, both emotions and motives, to the searching eye of God, submitting to such an examination and seeking no favours.

'Search' is a frequent request of the psalmist to God and is too the key word in all scientific and clinical research. In Psalm 139, for example, the request is for God to 'search me and know my heart', a heart open to the Lord's scrutiny (v 23). This then becomes a reality – 'thou hast searched me and known me' (v 1). God then is the one who searches the heart[9] and as he looks, as he searches, he sees more than is on the surface, the very deep, secret, places of a man's heart. So, what does this mean in reality?

5   Lamentation 3:40.
6   2 Corinthians 13:5, 6.
7   Matthew 9:12.
8   Psalm 26:2.
9   1 Samuel 16:7, 1 Chronicles 28:9, Jeremiah 17:10, Romans 8:27.

Patrick Woodhouse in his insightful Mowbray Lent Book for 2016 asks this question 'how easily we can be hidden and unknown, to ourselves as well as to others, a puzzle to ourselves' as though wearing our habitual masks our 'true face silenced'. Like Adam and Eve, in the garden attempting to hide from God and the question 'where are you?'

To return to Psalm 139. Pamela Greenberg's translation reads 'God, you have searched out my deepest places (the heart), you know what lies in my depth'. We are aware, and the Lord knows, how easy it is for us to lose our way, to become distracted, thrown off course, to say things we regret. Later in this psalm (v. 23) come the words 'search me with shovel and torchlight' (Greenberg). Sounds quite painful! The word 'shovel' is illuminating, as is torchlight! That same word comes in Job[10] where it is used of mining operations (iron and silver are taken from the earth) or of exploring a country[11] where the children of Dan elected five men to 'spy out' the land and to search it. So, this terrifying invitation to the Lord to examine our hearts with shovel and searchlight! And yet we do it with confidence in God's love and with relief that no part of our personality is hidden from the penetrating gaze of God. And this examination leads to a sense of wonder, joy and comfort.

---

10 Job 28:3.
11 Judges 18:2.

Z is for A to Z – the LOVING, COMPASSIONATE HEART OF GOD

'Consider the great love of the Lord . . . his love endures for ever.'[1]

'The heart of our God is full of mercy towards us.'[2]

But why Z (for A to Z) for the heart of God? We have come to the end of all the letters of the alphabet from beginning to end, a kind of alpha and omega. So, our perusal of the heart alphabet is, at least in one sense, complete. No need for any more letters! This triggers thoughts about the complete, huge, heart of God; there are no bounds to God's never-ending love. God is the source, the origin, of love. He is love in his 'inmost being', his essence, his heart. It is complete. As the old CSSM chorus has it – 'wide, wide as the ocean, high as the heavens above, deep, deep as the deepest sea is my Saviour's love'. Immense.

One of my first invitations to a World Congress of Cardiology was many years ago in Japan. The meeting itself was held in a huge hotel in Tokyo but, because this was too costly for my limited financial resources, I slept in the smallest hotel room imaginable – only just big enough to turn around in. Food and drink were very expensive but green tea was free; my introduction to this particular beverage, rich incidentally in heart-protective polyphenols. In the conference bag was an invitation – very unusual and never since seen in any other conference bag. An invitation to any Christians who might be participants and present at the Congress to meet for coffee each morning in the Japanese Garden. Among those I met was a Japanese Christian cardiologist whom I later visited in his home during a subsequent visit; we still correspond over forty years later. The invitation to coffee in the garden came from the 'resident hotel missionary', living with his family in a roof suite by invitation of the hotel management, I think as a ploy to attract to this particular hotel visitors from the USA. This missionary had been

---

1   Psalm 107:1.
2   Luke 1:78.

interned by the Japanese during WW2 but felt God's call to return after the war ended. He had not been treated well as a prisoner of war but, despite this, felt a deep love for the Japanese people. What kind of love was this? If this was a New Testament story the word used could well have been agape, unnatural love for his fellow man; unnatural in the sense that this kind of love is not possible for the natural man. It is a love that is the product of the Holy Spirit.

This Greek word *agape* is used of God's love for us, for example as in John's first letter, the statement 'God IS love'.[3] Love is the very heart of God. This is God's nature. Of course, God is also spirit, light, holy, just, almighty, creative: these are essential expressions for who God is but, of all these, it is this agape love that most clearly shows God's heart, what he is really like, his character and especially how he has revealed himself to the world.

And what is special about this kind of love? We think of love as that warm feeling, an emotion that one person feels for another and that loyally binds them to one another by 'heart and mind'. A deep warm affection, an attachment, a closeness which comes from the 'heart'. We, if we are fortunate in life, 'fall in love' – unsought and quite surprising – although with (most) human families in a sense inevitable, the love of parents for their children, the closeness of family ties. The New Testament has a word for this tender affection (*phileo*) which is word for, if we might put it this way, love for the lovable, for those we find attractive, for those we like, for those we chose to love, perhaps those who are most like us! Of course, love is deeper than that, as the passage in 1 Corinthians 13 makes clear, but it is not *agape* love. *Agape* love is love for the undeserving, the unlovable; not just for a particular chosen people. It is a love that does not discriminate, it is not partial, it is quite deliberate, and it involves a definite decision. The mind and will are involved; it is not just an emotional experience. It links what was said earlier about 'heart and mind'. It is this kind of love that we are commanded to have for our enemies.[4] It is unselfish, outgoing and sacrificial. And, it is active, the activity that led, quite wonderfully, to the sending of Jesus as a gift to an alien and undeserving world; and it was sacrificial in that it involved a deep loss for all three persons within the Godhead.

This love from the heart of God has always been apparent from the beginning of time. God loved, delighted in, the world he had created. A

---

3   1 John 4: 8, 16.

4   Matthew 5:44; Luke 6:35.

world created in love. 'God so loved the world'.[5] *Agape* love in the Old Testament is illustrated by the fact that God 'set his love upon' a people he had chosen, not because there was anything special about them[6] but because, as it is written, 'the Lord loves you'. This was a gift to a world[7] by deliberate choice, and yet to a human race, alienated from God and in opposition to him; a world certainly not intrinsically lovable.[8] This was a deep and constant love from a perfect Being towards most unworthy subjects.

The story of the prodigal son in Luke chapter 15 has been described as 'the greatest short story in the world'. It is third in the series of parables about lostness, which as Michael Sadgrove[9] has pointed out, is a recurring theme throughout Scripture and especially in its first two books. Of these three stories in Luke's gospel – the sheep (1 lost of 100), the coin (1 lost of 10) and, the most poignant of all, the son (1 lost of 2), this latter is where the 'shadow' of the father is most apparent. The younger son sets out alone and away from the father; a deliberate choice.

This son, at the start of the story, lived with his father, in the father's house, and yet despite the proximity to his father he left for a 'country' as far away from home as possible. This is a continuing story, one sadly not restricted to the days of youth or to the past. Sadly too, there are people once in the organised church, who despite a proximity to God the Father through countless times of worship, have also left, never to return; like the seed in another Jesus story that fell among thorns or into stony places. Why, I wonder should this be so? Perhaps 'coolness' of other church members, acting rather like the elder son in the parable, or a lack of pastoral support, dryness in the ministry of God's word or through the cares and worries of this world: even perhaps a justifiable over commitment to others, family members, the demands of elderly relatives. Yet missing out on the support the local church can give. Or, perhaps more likely, the attractiveness of what the outside world offers? Areas for discussion! Welcoming folk into the church (so important) and preventing them leaving by the back door! Wonderful when the 'prodigal' returns! Great cause for celebration!

5   John 3:16.
6   Deuteronomy 7:7, 8.
7   1 John 4:9, 10.
8   Romans 5:8.
9   Michael Sadgrove; *Lost Sons; God's Long Search for Humanity*, SPCK, 2012.

To return to the story itself. Although this has been sometimes referred to as the story of the loving father, neither of the two words or love (*agape* and *phileo*) are found in the text. The word used is compassion (*splanchna*) which means to have a concern for, a deep personal interest in the welfare and happiness of another and especially for the suffering and misfortunate, the lonely and the misunderstood. It is akin then to words like benevolence, generous, considerate. In physiology this word refers to the 'innards', the internal organs, the bowels, the intestines. In this sense it is used of the consequence of a physical fall.[10] The blood supply to these areas, which are sometimes referred to as 'one step lower than the heart' and which were once thought to be the seat of emotion, of passions, is called the splanchnic circulation.

In the biblical sense the word is used of the heart of Christ for individuals[11] and here in Luke for the attitude of affection of the father for the returned younger son.[12] This compassion is clearly active; the father is waiting, watching (never giving up hope), running (his heart pounding), embracing, his mind occupied with the 'next step' rather than listening to past history (no rebuke, no hesitation) all reflecting a compassionate heart. No standing on ceremony. It is a word linked elsewhere with tender mercy[13] affection[14] and forgiveness. Compassion driven by love; surely agape love since it was shown to both sons.

These three parables in Luke surely go together. They all have the same three main themes namely loss, seeking and then return with celebration and joy. It is not surprising then that they have been taken to illustrate the compassion and active love of God for mankind. He is the ever seeking, ever loving heavenly Father. There is always a welcome. This is the compassionate heart of our God.

I'm not a great lover of jazz; indeed, I know little about it, until that is until I picked up a compendium of 'Duke' Ellington recordings in a charity shop. There is a lovely story about this jazz legend, 'Duke' (Edward Kennedy) Ellington, which Alistair Cooke told in one of his weekly radio broadcasts called 'Letters from America'. As a regular listener (on a battery-operated

10 Acts 1:18.
11 Luke 7:13; 10:33.
12 Luke 15: 20.
13 Luke 1:78.
14 Philippians 1:8.

Roberts radio now still in use yet purchased over fifty years ago) I happened to hear this story in the 1970s.

It should be pointed out that Duke was in fact more than a jazz composer and interpreter. In an old (1962) review of classical recordings Peter Gammond called 'Duke' one of America's greatest composers, 'if George Gershwin is worthy of attention by classical critics, then Duke Ellington is doubly worth it'. He especially pointed out his 'remarkable recreation of Tchaikovsky's Nutcracker Suite' as an absolutely brilliant lesson in orchestration and harmony'. His fantastic jazz pianist Earl Hines practised for two to three hours each morning playing not 'blues' but the piano concertos of Mozart and Beethoven, 'just to keep his fingers loose'.

To return to the story! A few weeks before he died, when he was very sick indeed, Ellington sent to his friends a greeting card. On a field of blue was a cross made of four vertical letters and three horizontal letters. The central letter was O. The vertical word spelled 'LOVE' and the horizontal 'GOD'.

<pre>
    L
  G O D
    V
    E
</pre>

'Love, to make a cross, clear through the heart of God'. Is there I wonder a better, simpler illustration of God's very compassionate heart of love than the gift to us of his Son, Jesus and of his great work on the Cross of Calvary? 'God shows his love for us (poured into our hearts) in that even though we were still sinners (the ungodly) Christ died for us'.[15]

To close I quote a verse from another Timothy Dudley-Smith hymn:

> How vast is God's unfailing love
> to those by grace forgiven!
> it reaches to the skies above
> and scales the heights of heaven.

The complete, compassionate heart of God.

---

15 Romans 5:8.

A FINAL WORD ON TRANSLATIONS

I have used a variety of translations for the page footnote references: particularly the King James (AV) and the English Standard (ESV) versions. The ESV was first published in 2002 by Harper Collins: the edition I now use was produced by R L Allan & Son of Glasgow. The book title is taken from the ESV translation of Psalm 84:5 and reads 'Blessed are those whose strength is in you, in whose heart are the highways . . .' For the New Testament I have made extensive use of the *New Testament in Modern English for Schools* by J. B. Phillips first published by Geoffrey Bles Ltd in 1959 and still, to my mind, the clearest and most dynamic of all English NT translations. Sometimes in Scripture, the word for 'heart' (usually *leb* or *nephesh* in Hebrew and *kardia* or *psuche* in Greek) is translated as 'mind' or even 'soul'. For obvious reasons I have chosen the version which translates the word as heart! On page 92 there was a promise of suggestions for devotional commentaries. Among the best, covering the whole Bible, are any of the Crossway Bible Guides (published by Crossway Books) and the Scripture Union Daily Devotional Bible Commentary, originally published in four volumes by Scripture Union in 1974 and since reprinted. These commentaries are often out of print but well worth searching for.

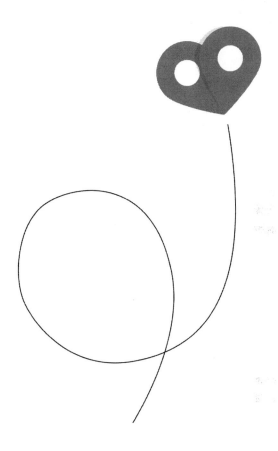

This closing picture is of the 'Eyes of the Heart' and is by Daniel Hough.
This heart is clearly on a highway journey. Upwards!